Stumbling towards
Enlightenment

Stumbling towards Enlightenment

A YOGA 101 COLLECTION

Shanan Harrell

SR SALT RIVER

SR

Salt River Publishing
Phoenix, Arizona
A Division of Wowkay Enterprises, LLC
www.SaltRiverPublishing.com

First edition 2010
Second revised edition 2014

16 15 14   5 4 3 2 1   III II

Cover and interior design: see Colophon

ISBN 978-0-9893349-4-5

CONTENTS

Local Color

Who's responsible for this?!?

This whole literary adventure is possible because Tammy Engel, Financial Goddess, introduced me to Claudia Henson, Newspaper Titan, at Don Juan's Restaurant one beautiful afternoon in my new hometown of Tehachapi, California. After we chatted for a moment, Claudia asked if I'd be interested in writing a yoga article for her local alternative paper, *The Loop*. I agreed and Yoga 101 was born. That was 2007.

I never dreamed I'd still be writing these things years later. Or that you'd be reading them. I never dreamed *anyone* would read them. But folks did and they eventually convinced me to slap a few columns together and call it a book. My greatest wish is that you enjoy this read. I hope it makes you smile. And laugh. And think.

By the way, after months of desperately trying to organize these literary nuggets into any kind of logical orderliness that some editors refer to as *chapters*, I have given up. I'm trusting you, as the Almighty Reader, to hack your way through these essays willy-nilly. No direction. No guidance. You might even call it stumbling…

My eternal
gratitude to
Claudia Henson
for continuing
to publish The
Mighty Loop;
Sam White for
putting up with
late submissions
and giving a gentle
guiding hand when
necessary; Carol
White for her
expertise and wise
counsel; Katy
Jacobson for her
cool photography
and willingness to
play along; Salt River Publishing for wanting to get my
book out to a wider audience; Gary Mazzola for his
patience and unwavering support; and all the Yoga Tribe
for their relentless encouragement and kindness.

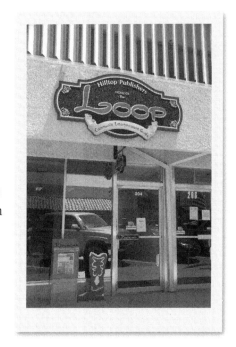

And, of course, a special mention to my beloved
family: Mimi, Sean, Cootie. No one loves you more
than me.

And with a deep sense of gratitude for the yoga and
the lineage of masters and teachers who have brought it
to us. May peace and peace and peace be everywhere...

Namaste, y'all

Yoga 101

The legend begins

12/2007

There are many causes that I am prepared to die for but no causes that I am prepared to kill for.

Mahatma Gandhi

AUTHOR'S NOTE: *This was the very first Yoga 101 article published in* The Loop.

They call me Yogashanan and I confess, I'm a yogaholic. (This is where the crowd responds, *Hi Yogashanan!*) I love the whole science of yoga. The whole eight-limbed system of yoga. I've spent years studying this ancient, transcendent practice and can't imagine my life without it.

Unfortunately, we in the West have picked out one aspect of this amazing system (the physical) and focused on it almost exclusively. Hence, the disturbing term *yoga butt*. But it's so much richer than that. Other than the physical poses, or asana, there are seven other limbs to the tree of yoga. Each one equally important. The eight limbs of the yogic tree look something like this:

3

Yama – Ethical practices for the yogi in the external world. The limb of yama contains five branches: non-violence, truthfulness, non-stealing, sexual moderation, and non-greed.

Niyama – Ethical practices for the yogi in his/her internal world. The limb of niyama also has five branches: purity, contentment, intense effort, self-study, devotion.

Asana – Physical freedom through physical poses.

Pranayama – Breath control.

Pratyahara – Withdrawal of the senses.

Dharana – One-pointed concentration.

Dhyana – Meditation.

Samadhi – Enlightenment.

Each of these limbs is reliant on the limb preceding it. From the first study of Yama to the final attainment of Samadhi, the limbs build upon each other in an intelligent, organized fashion. Back in the day when the students all wore loincloths and the ashes of their dead ancestors instead of Hugger-Mugger or Prana, a devotee was never taught Asana until years of practice had been dedicated to the ethical study of Yama and Niyama.

The first of the Yamas, and the concept on which all of yoga is built, is Ahimsa. Non-violence. Non-harming. No infliction of suffering or pain. But the idea of Ahimsa is more than just the absence of violence. It's about cultivating a consciousness of compassion and

kindness for all living beings. The entire work of Gandhi
was built on this one principle. The civil disobedience of
Martin Luther King was rooted in Ahimsa. Certainly the
amazing courage of the Bhutanese monks in recent times
has been a shining example of Ahimsa.

And even deeper than non-violent action, what
about non-violent thought? Words and thoughts can
be powerful weapons of pain. Am I practicing Ahimsa
when my inner voice is convincing me that I'm too
stupid, ugly, clumsy (the list goes on and on) to do
something that I'd really love to do? How about when I
glare at the person who has waaaay more than 15 items
in the express checkout? Whether it's something simple
like standing in line at the market or something more
challenging like standing on my head in my living room,
can I practice Ahimsa?

Years ago, I wrote a letter to the Pest Control Co.
that was spraying my suburban home on a monthly
poison fest. I wrote to terminate their services because
I was beginning a practice of non-violence and could
no longer, in good conscience, contribute to the murder
of thousands of living beings. I've often wondered
what it must have been like when the accounting guy
read the letter out loud to the other guys in the office
and you know they just laughed their heads off. Well,
good. I'm delighted to have given them a good guffaw.
I was doing my part in the proliferation of Ahimsa. I
was a warrior for peace. By god, I was a young and
budding Yogashanan.

Some folks think I can overdo the non-violence thing.
I've spent more time than I'm willing to admit trying

to scoop up a spider from the empty bathtub before
drowning the unsuspecting arachnid. I once dated a
guy that would kill flies between his bare hands with
a quick, mighty, murderous smack. (Don't ask.) After
witnessing that first fatal fly smack, I knew our days as a
couple were numbered.

By contrast, I also have friends who will pull over
their car to rescue a snake stuck on Hwy 202. Saving
stuck snakes is an opportunity unique to Tehachapians.
I mean, really, how many folks can say they practice
compassion by saving potential reptile roadkill? Ahimsa
in action on the streets of Tehachapi.

So now the yoga training begins. Think on not harm-
ing, not hurting or causing pain. *Particularly to yourself.*
Consider not even being purposefully annoying. Try it
for one day. Heck, try it for one hour. Become aware of
your own tendency towards harmful thought, speech
or actions. Instead, practice Kindness. The Dalai Lama
once said that his whole spiritual practice could be
wrapped up in one word: Kindness.

Notes on a wolf parable

Who's hungry?

There's this very cool old Native American parable that I love. And I'm sure I'll butcher the poetry of the story, but it goes something like this...

Many moons ago, somewhere in the magnificent golden hills and verdant valleys of Tehachapi, a grandfather was counseling a grandson when he said, "There are two wolves living inside me. One wolf is agitated. He is angry, fearful. Pacing back and forth, terrified. The other wolf is loving. He is warm, tranquil. Dancing back and forth, open-hearted. These two wolves are forever doing battle within me to win my attention."

The boy asked, "And which one wins?"

The grandfather answered, "Whichever one I feed."

Now that's a cool story. (I get a mental visual of these two beautiful and powerful wolves twisting and turning inside my head. Each desperately trying to overthrow the other. Each trying to cleverly win the prize of the mind's attention.) Whichever one I feed. Come on. That's good.

And so I begin to ponder, which wolf do I feed on
a consistent basis? What's getting my attention? What
stories have I fed over the years? You've heard the old
saying, *You are what you eat.* Well, let's take that a bit
further on down the line and propose, *You are what you
think.* Think you're a healthy, happy yogi with a bright
and promising future? Congratulations! You're right.
Think you're a big fat pathetic loser without a hope in
this cruel world to ever find even one tiny shred of happiness? Congratulations! You're right. (I have personally
held both of these beliefs at some point in my journey.)

Change your thinking, change your life.

One of my biggest beliefs about myself, a wolf that
I feed pretty generously, is that I can't sing. I am multi-
talented in oh, so many ways, but singing has never been
one of them. I have always lamented the fact that I have
no musical talents. I love to sing in the car or shower
or whatever and I have a brilliantly talented boyfriend
who sings like an angel, but when my brilliantly talented
boyfriend tries to harmonize some tune with me, I completely lose it and go off into a parallel auditory universe
and we both ultimately end up in a crumpled heap on
the floor. (But that's another story.)

So, if I begin to change my mind about my singing
capability, do you think that might work? I'm reminded
of Linda McCartney back during the Wings heyday.
Everyone knew she couldn't sing, but Paul just loved her
so much he put her up there and we all accepted her as
if she had one drop of talent. I wonder, what were her
thoughts on her musical competence? Which wolf did
she feed?

Maybe that will happen with my BTB (brilliantly talented boyfriend). I can sing along and will be accepted because we're just so nauseatingly cute together. (And we're old and crazy in love.) And then my mental state, my wolf being fed, will be that I can sing. I will reperceive myself as a singer and perhaps my singing will improve. Or not. That's the other thing about yoga, we can't be attached to the outcome. God bless Linda McCartney.

So consider these wolves. What are yours? Who do you feed? Can you reperceive something about yourself? Be diligent in your *right thinking*. Practice is at the heart of all yoga, so practice feeding the wolf which brings you the most happiness. Practice expanding those self-imposed limits of who you are. Change your mind. Change your life.

Notes on petroglyphs

The universe and its inhabitants
are as ephemeral as the clouds in the sky;
Beings being born and dying
are like a spectacular dance or drama show.
The duration of our lives is like a flash of lightning
or a firefly's brief twinkle;
Everything passes like the flowing waters
of a steep waterfall.

The Buddha

I recently hiked the China Lake Naval Weapons Station Petroglyph Canyon. That is not a misprint.

In nearby Ridgecrest, on land now managed by the U.S. Navy, lies the greatest concentration of petroglyphs in the U.S. of A. In fact, I think the Museum Guy may have even mentioned all of North America. Petroglyphs are Native American works of art. They are images that have been literally carved, pecked, or scratched into solid rock. The images cover both sides of the canyon sometimes at unbelievable heights. They are depictions of things of great importance to the tribe, some recognizable, some not so much. Bighorn sheep, family groupings, shaman, warriors, sun, stars.

The oldest drawings date back an unbelievable 16,500 years. That's like a really, really long time ago. As I stare at the designs, I realize I'm standing in the same spot where another human stood, carving away, when the planet was a very different kind of home and Life was a very different kind of experience. The ancientness of the place is palpable. The sacredness, profound.

As I spent more time with these primitive drawings, I was reminded of the yogic concept of impermanence. Impermanence is the principle that nothing stays the same, all things inevitably change. Everything comes and goes. Life is in a constant state of flux. Every experience is transitory. (Our suffering is caused when we try to attach to anything, try to keep it from changing, try to keep things the same.)

The law of Impermanence led me to think about what these grounds would be like another 3,000 years from now. What would the typical "tourist" look like? How would they travel? Would they think about or care that in 2008, a yoga teacher from Tehachapi with three companions stood at these very rocks and awed over the ancestral Oneness of us all? Or will there even be a planet or Petroglyph Canyon to peruse?? Will impermanence then include the disappearance of the Earth from the Universe? Maybe. And I began to truly appreciate my own small and insignificant place in all this. How liberating. How freeing. How brilliant.

Another question the Petroglyphs brought up for me: If I were to carve images of the things that were most important to me on the face of a canyon, what would I draw? What would I want people to know about me 3,000 years from now? Certainly, I'd draw my family. My mom and the kids. Yoga poses. My mala beads. My boyfriend and me holding hands. A coffee cup. A full box of Tofutti Cuties. And what would the future folks think of these items? What would you draw?

Another observation: the drawings would appear or disappear according to the light. When we first arrived, my friend was looking for a very specific sundial calendar that she had admired on her previous visit. We found the general area, but the calendar was not very visible. She lamented how last time the dial had been so clear, it was like it had been drawn last week. When we were leaving the canyon several hours later and passed by the site of the dial again, she yelped with joy as she saw her precious calendar revealed in the light of the afternoon.

(Personal Observation: the drawing was always there. If we search for it in a certain light, it may not be visible. Change the positioning of the light or the perception of the mind and suddenly things become clear.)

So when I get behind a slow big rig on Hwy 202, or the ATM is out of order, or the market is sold out of Tofutti Cuties, I think back to the petroglyphs and remember that 3,000 years from now – heck, three minutes from now – these momentary nuisances will have ebbed. Impermanence reminds me that *this, too, shall pass*. And the sooner I can take this notion to heart, the more peaceful I can be.

Notes on critical mass

*There's a statistical theory that if you give
a million monkeys typewriters and set them
to work, they'd eventually come up with the
complete works of Shakespeare.*

Ian Hart

In his book *The Hundredth Monkey*, Ken Keyes wrote
about scientists who had been observing monkeys in the
wild for thirty years. The scientists provided monkeys
with sweet potatoes that had been dropped in sand.
The monkeys liked the potatoes but found the sand
unpleasant.

One day, one clever young monkey washed her
potatoes in a nearby stream. She taught the trick to her
mother and her playmates, who taught it to their mothers. As the story goes, perhaps 99 monkeys learned to
wash their sweet potato.

Eventually the 100th monkey joined in. Suddenly,
almost every monkey on the island began to wash their
potatoes before eating them. The added energy of this

100th monkey had somehow created a behavioral breakthrough.

And, *even more amazing*, the scientists observed that the act of washing sweet potatoes had jumped over the sea, because colonies of monkeys on other islands, *as far as 500 miles away*, began washing their sweet potatoes.

This phenomenon is known as "critical mass." When a limited number of people know something in a new way, it remains the conscious property of only those people. However, there is a point at which if only one more person tunes in to a new awareness, that new awareness is picked up by everyone. The awareness becomes part of the overall consciousness.

So what does all this monkey business (pun intended) have to do with yoga? Yoga is rooted in training the mind. Cultivating awareness. Being fully conscious. Critical Mass Theory is a fascinating discovery in the *connectedness of all thought*. And it has proven to be an important tool for social change.

Consider the critical mass of cigarette smoking. Up until recently, smoking was considered hip. All the cool people smoked, which of course included Yours Truly. The media was filled with images of sexy, desirable smokers. Then along came the party-pooping Surgeon General. People were dying of lung cancer, heart disease and emphysema. Hmmmm. Not so sexy. We monkeys began to shun cigarettes.

And then, somewhere about 1972, the 100th monkey shifted her perception and poof! The once wildly popular Marlboro Man has slunk away in a hacking, coughing cloud of humiliation. Critical mass? Check!

I'm sensing new critical mass waves developing. Certainly energy consumption is one. That ginormous gas guzzling Expedloration is no longer as hip as it was. The race issue? Now that we have an African American president, I mean, *come on*. (Although I did see a confederate flag waving proudly from a license plate frame just this morning.) Can you throw your MacTrash out the car window without a thought to the health of our planet? Critical mass is gathering and teetering on the precipice of social change for the benefit of all. We're becoming informed through the spreading, broadening consciousness of our global community.

How many times have you asked yourself, when faced with the overwhelming suffering in the world, what can I do? Well, here's something I can do. Be that 100th monkey. Shift my attention from feeling impotent and hopeless to feeling empowered and optimistic. In the shifting of my attention, I am joining forces with like-minded others and forming that wave of awareness that can bring healing and wholeness to our world.

Wake up and smell the gasoline. Be the 100th monkey for the greening of our nation and economy. Be the 100th monkey for equanimity for all living beings. Be the one who turns the tide from the darkness towards the light, from ignorance to awareness, from fear to love.

I can be the 100th monkey *or* I can jump in the Hummer, fire up that Marlboro, throw the empty pack out the window, and burn rubber to the nearest war rally.

Nah, this monkey is taking her sweet potato to the river…

What's PEZ got to do with it?

Candy is dandy.
But meditation won't rot your teeth.

Yogashanan

Meditation is a significant part of any yoga practice.
When learning meditation, and as a longtime practitioner, it's important to remember that the mind has an
active nature and will continually be busy with ideas,
thoughts, and plans even as we endeavor to quiet it.
The mind loves to organize, categorize, criticize. One
good and common instruction for meditation is to allow
the thoughts to just float by, without giving them any
attention. Just notice and let them go.

In practicing this noticing and letting go, visualiza-
tions can be helpful. For instance, clouds floating by do
not disturb the sky, so thoughts floating by do not need
to disturb the mind. Visualize leaves floating in a stream
while keeping your attention on the flowing water and
not the leaves themselves. You know, sweet little mental
games to assist in the practice of calming and simply
observing the mind's endless activity. Meditation is not

trying to stop the thoughts, it's the practice of observing those thoughts with detachment. Then, there's room for exploration. Room for those aha moments of glory and brilliance.

So one day I'm sitting on my bolster in present awareness contemplation. I'm watching the clouds float by. I'm hearing the cars zoom by as the road is undisturbed by their travel. The leaves are floating but my attention stays with the water. I try to dwell in the space between the thoughts and not get caught up in the thoughts themselves. All the usual techniques. And then, with absolutely no foreshadowing, no warning whatsoever, came my flash of glory and brilliance. My aha! moment of overwhelming magnitude. Not clouds, not cars, not leaves. PEZ. Yes, PEZ.

I googled *pez*. That's when I learned that the name is always in all caps: PEZ. Like you're screaming PEZ out to the unconscious world. For your information and wonderment, PEZ was first marketed as a compressed peppermint sweet in Vienna around 1927. The name PEZ was derived from the letters at the start, the middle and the end of the German word for peppermint, *Pfefferminz*, the first PEZ flavor.

As any self-respecting PEZ dweeb knows, there are over 550 different PEZ dispensers: Star Trek. NASCAR. Pirates of the Caribbean. In 2007 a limited edition Elvis set was released featuring three dispensers from different time periods in Presley's life. (Can the Michael Jackson PEZ be far behind?) Even bride/groom PEZ. Now that's romance, my friends. What bride doesn't *dream* of the ultimate PEZ couple sitting atop her wedding cake?

There's also the international convention held in Ohio each year, PEZ-A-MANIA. For our Jewish friends, there's *kosher* PEZ in specialty markets. If you are traveling to the San Francisco Bay Area, you'll want to make time to visit the Burlingame Museum of PEZ Memorabilia.

My personal favorite, though, was the candy "truck dispensers" that were created specifically for the last presidential campaign. You could have your choice of John McCain OR Barack Obama for PEZident. PEZident. I got a good chortle on that one. And I also admired the PEZ folks' equanimity in not favoring one candy-date. Get it, candy-date. Like candidate. Hahahahahahahahaha.

Anyhoo, this idea of PEZ as meditation tool. Each thought popping up, with the next one moving up in line right behind it. An endless stream of thoughts just like the endless stream of PEZ. And just as there are hundreds of different styles of meditation, there are hundreds of different dispensers of PEZ. The dispensers (external forms) are created to appeal to our individual preferences. I would prefer, say, the Princess Leia, while my BF would probably prefer Movie Star Elvis or Captain Picard. I resonate with a vipassana style meditation while someone else prefers Zen style.

The candy, however, is the same within each dispenser. Each little brick of sugary goodness tries to grab my attention as I concentrate on simply observing the flow of candies from the gullet of Hello Kitty or Yosemite Sam. The dispenser can change, but the candy is always the same, always flowing. And it will be the same, eternally. Since 1927.

Yogashanan is dead, long live Yogashanan

You're traveling through another dimension, a dimension not only of sight and sound but of mind. You're moving into a land of both shadow and substance, of things and ideas. That's the signpost up ahead – your next stop, the Twilight Zone.

TIME: Recently. A peaceful, beautiful morning.

PLACE: My office.

I sit at my laptop, as I have a thousand times before, to read the morning emails. I enter my screen name and password.

Screen name and password invalid.

Re-enter. Same message. Try again. Same. I unplug and re-plug everything, just like my techie BF has taught me. Re-start.

Screen name and password invalid.

I eventually phone AOL.

AOL: Greetings! Thank you for calling AOL. My
       name is Johnny. How may I assist you?

ME: Hey, Johnny. My email password isn't
       working.

AOL: Yes, of course, Miss. Let's look up your
       account. Your screen name?

ME: Yogashanan. (I spell it.)

AOL: Hmmmmm. I don't seem to find that
       account. Please re-spell it for me?

I re-spell my name a few hundred times. Johnny keeps
looking to no avail.

AOL: I'm sorry, Miss Yogashanan. There's no
       record of you in our system.

ME: But that's impossible. I've been using that
       name since 1997. It *must* be there.

AOL: I'm so sorry, Miss Yogashanan.

ME: But you don't understand. I have all my
       contacts, my saved files, records for my
       business! It can't just vanish into cyber-
       space, Johnny!!

AOL: I understand, Miss Yogashanan. But how
       can I help you when there's no record of
       you in our files? I'm so sorry.

ME: Listen, Johnny, if that is your real name,
       you can wipe that smirk I'm hearing right

off your face. I can't just lose *all* my email account info. It will be devastating to my business. Much less my stellar personal life.

AOL: I'm so sorry, Miss Yogashanan. Is there anything else I can help you with today?

ME: But Johnny, you haven't helped me with *this*!

AOL: I am so sorry for your difficulty. Is there anything else I can do for you today?

ME: (Click.)

My eyes well with tears as I realize that I don't exist. I've been disappeared. Vaporized. Game over. I try to get clever and sign in as a new member and ask for the screen name Yogashanan. I learn that it's already in use. Well, yeah, nitwads, I'm the one using it except I don't exist!! Somebody cue Rod Serling. I've just crossed over into the Twilight Zone.

Then, sweetly, there's a momentary sense of freedom. Of lightness from the weight of all that personal history. Liberation from years of information! Without my history, who am I? Without my records, who am I? Do I really use my email account info to define who I am? And doesn't that seem just a bit limiting and deeply pathetic?

I'm reminded of how the current economic atmosphere has forced many to question the very core of their identity. After a lifetime of conditioning that we *are* our bank account or career or possessions, we're experiencing a newfound confusion as those things fall away. How do I define myself now? If I'm not the bread-winner, who am I? If I lose all my email accounts with their years of collected stuff, who am I? While Bernie Madoff rots in jail and I'm left without my retirement, who am I?

And how long will I need to sit in the undeniable sad-ness of losing my beloved (yet inherently false) identity before I can get on with things? (Personally, I had a cute little meltdown that afternoon and then went about rebuilding my budding empire of world domination.)

Yoga encourages us to ponder the Big Questions. Who am I? Beyond name, job, family of origin, social status, or even the predictable *child of the Universe* or *spiritual being having a human experience* stuff. The yogi just keeps asking sincerely and listening deeply. And then asks again. All the while understanding that the current screen name and password may someday be invalid.

Distraction as guru

You talkin' to me?
Travis Bickel

*Tehachapi single mom discovers secret to brighter,
whiter teeth! Find out how Angelina Jolie stays
so thin! (It used to be Meg Ryan. Not sure what
happened there.) Lose 35 lbs. of stomach fat in three
weeks! Marrying an inmate? We go to most prisons
in California!*

These slogans have become my new inspirations for
practice as I navigate my way through the daily newsletters I receive from Beliefnet.com. Serving the spiritual
communities of *all* religions with blogs and articles and
bulletin boards and all that groovy cyberstuff, Beliefnet
is a wealth of information for all spiritual traditions.

I subscribe to two of their daily newsletters, Buddhist
Wisdom and Hindu Wisdom. I have always enjoyed
these daily shots of insight, finding them inspirational
and thought-provoking as I nurse my morning cup
of coffee. Until recently. Until the marketing vultures
descended and conspired to eat my brain.

These days, as I open the newsletters, I am instantly greeted by a ginormous pop-up with heartbreaking head shots of starving children. Simply click on the starving child of my choice and make a difference. The pop-up is large enough to hide the text of the newsletter and I am flushed with shame as I click the close button and the desperate faces disappear.

As I scroll down the newsletter, there's another ad to grab my attention. This one features an underwear-clad female torso that transforms from lumpy folds of cellulite-dimpled flab to sleek, slim abs of steel in stop-motion graphics with the tagline of something like *Disgusted with your weight? Lose 35 lbs. of belly fat in three weeks!* Beside the perpetually flashing belly is a magical female face that morphs from old, wrinkled prune to smooth, clear peach to broadcast how the *top three anti-wrinkle creams really, really work!*

I am deeply saddened. And highly annoyed. These starving children and fat, aging women are blocking access to my daily dose of spiritual wisdom. How will I possibly gain any insight from this newsletter now that it's shape-shifted from a simple, sweet reminder for my spiritual practice into a blatant, attention-sucking ad whore? And I don't mean in a good way.

I am discouraged by the overt commercialism of the flashing ads. Why can't I just read my Hindu prayer post in peace without a pulsating, vibrating visual billboard clamoring for my attention? I curse the incessantly flaring belly and Dr. Oz's secret formula to transform me into Angelina Jolie. I wonder if folks really click on the flashing prison cell to find the perfect minister for their Big

House nuptials. Is that clever Tehachapi single mom truly eager to share her secrets for teeth whitening with me? Why is Beliefnet set on disrupting my peace of mind?

I realize I have met my new guru, Sri Sri Electronic Distraction. She works very hard so I can have the opportunity to practice patience. She flips and flops and shimmies around the page vying for my attention as I struggle to maintain concentration on the sage advice of the ancient masters. As the ads dance all around me, I close my eyes, breathe into my irritation and bring myself back to the present moment. As the tubby abdomen inflates and deflates, I inhale and exhale. Can I take it all in without the grinding urge to smack the face of the old/young woman as she wrinkles/smoothes her way to beauty? Can I somehow use these annoyances as mindfulness tools?

Just as in meditation practice, when the attention wanders, I must bring it back to the breath. So when the jiggling belly becomes too fascinating for me to ignore, I return to the breath. When my concern over my own aging face allows my mind to get caught up, I return to the breath. When I get crazy excited about having Angelina Jolie's perfectly thin body and the wedding of my dreams at San Quentin, I return to the breath. Distraction as guru. Annoyance as teacher. Yoga as guide. Breath as anchor.

Lone Star stunned

*Life in Lubbock, Texas, taught me two things:
One is that God loves you and you're going to
burn in hell. The other is that sex is the most
awful, filthy thing on earth and you should save
it for someone you love.*

Butch Hancock

Sigh. My Texas heritage is weighing heavily on me these days. Being a Texan has always been a mixed blessing, a baffling fusion of beautiful sweetness and dark mystery.

I recognize that Texans are quirky. For starters, we like to plaster the shape of our state all over everything. You can't drive a neighborhood without spying some spunky lawn art in the familiar shape of the Lone Star State. My mother has a Texas-shaped gold pinky ring with a diamond right at Big D. We are the home of drive-thru liquor stores and the mechanical bull. We have the highest density of churches as well as the highest rate of death penalty executions. Texans are the kindest, friendliest folks you can possibly imagine.

Unless they're racist homophobic extremist nut jobs. And often we're both.

And you thought the Tehachapi School Board had problems? Ha! That whole silly $150,000 recall is a drop in the bucket compared to the recent hijinks of the Texas Board of Education. In case you haven't heard, the TBE is rewriting history books to reflect a more conservative-friendly point of view. Decisions by the Board can affect textbook content *nationwide* because Texas is one of publishers' biggest clients. Holy cow patty!

In the new textbook standards, some of the more fascinating updates recommended by the Board would include the U.S. government being described as a *constitutional republic* rather than *democratic*. Board members argued about the classification of historic periods (still BC and AD, rather than BCE. and CE) and decided to delete a sociology requirement focusing on institutional racism and its presence in American society.

Thomas Jefferson will no longer be included among influential writers of the nation's intellectual origins. So that whole Jeffersonian Enlightenment era thing? Unimportant nonsense. (Jefferson, a deist who helped pioneer the legal theory of the separation of church and state, is *not* a model founder in the Board's judgment.) In fact, the Board refused to require that "students learn that the Constitution prevents the U.S. government from promoting one religion over others."

And my personal favorite tweak, Joe McCarthy was right! He was just tragically misunderstood while doing his best to eradicate the demon Communism from our fair land. As Don McLeroy, the dentist leader of the Board's conservative faction put it in last year's debate over evolution, "Somebody's got to stand up to experts." Really, y'all?

And then there's Randy Neugebauer (R-Tex.) who yelled "Baby killer!" during the healthcare debate on the floor of the U.S. House of Representatives. Southern gentleman charm at its finest. He has since apologized while insisting that he was referring to the bill and not Rep. Bart Stupak (D-Mich.) who was speaking at the time.

What's happened to my home state? Did all the smart people move away because they're smart enough to know better? Each day seems to bring some new and horrifying embarrassment. Texas has become the drunk uncle of the U.S. family. The one that everyone dreads seeing turn up for the holiday party because we know, we just *know*, that something deeply disturbing is going to transpire. Especially after a beer or two or seven. Then, drunk on ignorance, Uncle Texas goes spewing and slurring his way across the American front lawn until he finally does a face plant into the shrubbery. Spunky Texas-shaped lawn art smashed to smithereens. The rest of the family watches in horror and shakes their heads. What do we do with Uncle Texas?

For the time being, I'm determined to practice patience and acceptance. Patience and acceptance. Patience and acceptance. And I wonder, is there a possibility of intervention? Could we, as Texas' concerned loved ones, come bursting into the trailer park, yelling

"Knowledge killer!" and drag him off to Common Sense Rehab for an undetermined period of time until he wakes up and smells his brain rotting? Wouldn't that be the most loving thing to do??

But, then, as the saying goes, Don't Mess With Texas. You could find yourself with a first-class ticket on the Execution Express. Erased from history. Just like that Jesus-hating dimwit, Thomas Jefferson. *Fun killer!*

Careful what you make fun of

We change, whether we like it or not.
Ralph Waldo Emerson

My longtime friend Dan is one of the smartest people I've ever known. He's a professional writer, cultural expert and just all-round intellectually gigantic guy. On the physical side, he's been a tennis player for most his adult life and would never consider going to a gym or athletic club or any kind of organized mirrored boy/girl workout exercising facility. He's made it clear to me that only open-mouth breathers do that sort of thing. Superficial. Mindless. Intellectuals just don't *do* the gym. We play tennis. We bowl.

After a year of not seeing my friend, I ran into Dan and was overwhelmed by the change in his physical appearance. He was fit. Tight. Hard.

"Dude!" I gushed. "What's going on? You look amazing!!"

"My shame knows no bounds. I joined a gym and I've been working out. I never miss a day. I'm completely hooked… It's beyond pathetic. I've turned into the person that I used to make fun of."

I laughed hard. What a wonderful notion. *I've turned into the person that I used to make fun of.*

My mom is a most unique and delightful character. She's a Texan through and through. Pet owners have always been a source of irritation for her. For years I've heard her wail, "I talked to (fill in the blank) today. You know, I love her and all, but if I have to hear one more story about her animals, I'm gonna puke. [My mom always likes using the word *puke*.] I'm sorry but I just don't give a hoot if Cuppy had a big day at the doggie park with all the other precious little doggies and how they made friends and romped together and sniffed each other. Why do pet owners always think that someone else is even slightly interested in their pet's latest endearing adventure??!!"

Enter Molly. A two-year-old adorable, übersweet cockapoo/lhasapso/foofie mix rescue dog that a mutual friend encouraged her to adopt. As you can only imagine, my mom now sings a bit of a different tune. Just recently, as she sat at her breakfast table regaling me with Molly's latest achievements, I looked her straight in the eye with a sly grin and accused her, "Do you hear yourself? Do you realize what's happened to you? You've become the person that you used to make fun of."

She stopped mid-sentence and looked right back at me. Deer in the proverbial headlights. "You're right. OMG. You're right." Then she went on with her story, unfazed.

I love this notion of becoming the person you used to make fun of. (It has surely happened to us all.) And can we use this realization to blast open our judgments? Understanding that in five years (or five months or five minutes) we may become the person that we judge so harshly today? So perhaps we can ease up on those judgments and get it that we're not a fixed entity. What works today doesn't necessarily work tomorrow. We are fluid and flexible and our perceptions change. This is the law of Impermanence at work.

Becoming the person that you used to make fun of also helps build compassion, understanding and tolerance. One of my personal experiences with this idea involves karaoke. I have always hated and dreaded the torture of karaoke. I found it painful and embarrassing and just generally demeaning for everyone concerned. Then I inexplicably dated a guy who loved karaoke (don't ask). I eventually came to appreciate the courage that radiates from any karaoke lounge. *I've become the person that I used to make fun of.* Or, better yet, because I could never have the same courage that they possess, *I'm weaker than the person that I used to make fun of.*

So, consider your judgments about people. Not just individuals, but large groups. Entire communities. Can you imagine becoming one of them? Thinking the way they do? Seeing things from their perspective?

It's all about recognizing the Oneness and Goodness in us all.

That's the practice. That, and belting out your best Grace Slick *White Rabbit* at the local karaoke bar.

In praise of the quickie

So little time and so little to do.
Oscar Levant

Meditation has countless definitions and interpretations. A few I like are: the uninterrupted flow of concentration; an internal state of relaxed awareness; the turning or revolving of a subject in the mind; a quiet, alert, powerfully concentrated state wherein new knowledge and insights are awakened from within as awareness focuses one-pointedly on an object or specific line of thought. And my personal fave: a state of pure present-moment awareness. Not dwelling in the past or dreaming of the future. Just *now*. This moment. And this one. And this one. And, yeah, this one, too.

Meditation is considered a practice that requires *time* to be quiet and reflective. *Time* to sit silently on my cushion and gaze at a candle flame or repeat a mantra as I finger my mala beads or observe my breath. I lovingly prepare my altar with candles, incense, offerings. I read sacred texts. It's my ritual to set the scene just right. And if my karma ship comes in, perhaps I'll receive a new insight or understanding or even a defrag of my mental muck. Happy day! Wonder of wonders!

But mostly it's the routine of lighting the candle, burning the incense, setting the offerings and reading and fingering. (For the inquiring mind, *fingering the mala* is the act of passing one bead over the fingertips with each repetition of the mantra. Just so you know and don't make any unseemly assumptions. Or hey, assume away. Whatever rocks your world.)

So I'm at a meditation workshop and the teacher introduces the idea of *short bursts, many times*. Short bursts, many times? It's his theory that anytime we are stopped by something that takes our breath away or stuns us into awe or jerks us out of our sleepy mind and into present-moment awareness, that's meditation too. Anytime we are in a state where our attention becomes consumed by an object, that's it. That's it? Really? Seems a little too simple. Don't I need to set the holy scene? Burn something? Or at least sit with crossed legs and chant Sanskrit for a minimum of 30 minutes??

While rushing out the front door one day, I'm suddenly overtaken by the incredible beauty of a flock of turkey vultures flying overhead. The vast group alights in my neighbor's tree. There are about 50 of them delicately balanced on the tips of the branches and I am spellbound. Filled with deep awe and appreciation. I'm not in the future, I'm not in the past, I'm completely present in my concentration on the birds. For several minutes, I am fully awake and aware. Aha! That's what the teacher is talking about. Short bursts, many times.

I'm taking the garbage out at dusk, arms fully loaded, and suddenly there's the sunset. The tone of the sky is undeniably sacred. It practically demands my attention. And there I am, mid-yard with arms full of trash, locked eyes with the sky. I'm transformed for a few moments as I become one with the nature of the sunset. Or sunrise for that matter. Short bursts, many times.

I am struggling to load my car with stuff for an event. The stuff is heavy and awkward and my Internal Complainer is pretty busy. As I'm struggling out to the car, I happen to notice an ant on my driveway. She is carrying a stick that is about 10 times her size and it is heavy and awkward and she is struggling, too. I'm instantly snapped out of my monkey mind by this beautiful, determined creature. For a few moments, I am one with my struggling sister ant. Short bursts, many times.

I find these short flashes, these aha! moments, these spiritual quickies, if you will, infinitely astonishing. I don't have to burn anything or read anything or, for that matter, finger anything. I only need broaden my consciousness to actually see what's in front of me. Turkey vultures! Sunrise/set! Tiny brave and brilliant creatures! All tools for meditation.

Of course, I have not abandoned my existing practice. I continue to sit and gaze and finger, but I'm also available for that short burst. Eyes open, heart open, mind open. Blast off!

Notes on giveaway

I have found that among its other benefits,
giving liberates the soul of the giver.

Maya Angelou

Recently I was invited to a party which included a
"Giveaway." A "Giveaway" is choosing something of
your own that you consider special or of great value but
now you are ready to pass on to someone else. It is most
definitely not the typical white elephant exchange. This
Giveaway practice has some meaning, some merit. How
marvelous! Giving a personal treasure away is certainly
no problem for a highly accomplished yogi like me.
Non-attachment is my middle name.

I open my closet and spot a forgotten, yet beloved
scarf. Ah, yes, that would be perfect. It was given to
me by a dear friend and it has cool Sanskrit writing
all over it. Yeah, that's... the... one... well, maybe not.
I really love that scarf and it's loaded with memories.
Nah, not the scarf. In fact, I think I'll wear the scarf. Ah,
yes, it looks so beautiful on me! So, on to the next item.
Uh, no, not my Spin Doctors World Tour 1997 t-shirt.

How about… well… no, not that either. I made my way through two closets before I came up with something that I felt appropriate.

This whole Giveaway idea was beginning to annoy me. After all, I've always considered myself a generous girl. In years past, I've cleaned my closets regularly and given my discards to charity. And, boy, was I ever proud of my amazing generosity and non-attachment! But then I began to see how it's easy to be generous with crap that I no longer want (Billy Bass plaque, anyone?).

But when I'm asked to give something that actually has value for me, something that I truly hold dear, well, mister, that's another story. My amazing generosity sputters and coughs to a selfish standstill. My attachments become swollen and painfully obvious. I am reminded of the Simpsons episode where Homer gives Marge (who doesn't bowl) a bowling ball for her birthday with HOMER engraved across the top. D'oh!!

What is *authentic* generosity? The willingness to give unwanted items away? The willingness to share, but only when there's plenty available? How about putting restrictions on the gift? Does that still count as a virtue? Not so much. Now consider the capacity to give unconditionally, wholeheartedly. The willingness to give even your treasured scarf to another. The willingness to share your last bite of chocolate. A genuine concern for the happiness of others coupled with non-attachment. A lofty goal, to be sure.

By the by, the item I eventually chose for the Giveaway was a small antique mirror that I had owned with my first (and now deceased) husband. As I presented my hostess with the gift, she sweetly smiled. She said she'd been having a weepy day even though her house was filled with people she loved. She had found it easy to express that love to everyone in the room; everyone, that is, except herself. Except the girl she was now seeing in the beloved mirror. The mirror that had once reflected love for me was now reflecting love right back at her.

And that, my friends, is the magic of authentic generosity.

Would Jesus drink coffee?

Blessed is the man who expects nothing,
for he shall never be disappointed.

Alexander Pope

Recently I have had the great privilege of teaching a
group of students who are aspiring teachers. We have
covered all kinds of good information concerning the
proper alignment of asana (poses), the philosophy of
yoga, and teaching technique. The students are mostly
younger than me (but who isn't these days?) and are
filled with excitement. Last week as I entered the studio
to begin our day's work, I had a Starbucks cup with me.
Before I began class, one student timidly raised her hand
and sheepishly asked me what was in the cup. When I
replied "coffee," there was a collective gasp as if all the
air in the room had been instantly sucked out.

I looked at the horror on their faces and realized I
had just shattered their image of their yoga teacher. Real
yogis don't drink coffee. Coffee is bad. It's practically
immoral. How can our teacher justify the fact that she
drinks coffee? Would Krishna drink coffee? Would Jesus

drink coffee? Would Buddha drink coffee? I smiled at them and said, "Hey, it's just a cup of joe."

This experience reminded me of my own trauma several years ago when I attended a seminar led by a group of Tibetan Buddhist monks. When we broke for lunch, I followed them through the cafeteria line where they loaded up their plates with chicken. Chicken! Monks eating meat? Impossible. All monks are vegetarian. I'm sure that's written in the monk rules of law somewhere, right?

A friend of mine tells the story of a group of diverse spiritual practitioners who made a pilgrimage to a temple and decided to sit together in the large meditation hall for prayer. As the group settled in, one particular woman remarked to one of the monks that the statue of the golden Buddha bothered her and was making it difficult for her to pray. He nodded and immediately took the statue from the altar and repositioned it into a nearby closet. "Better now?" he humbly asked. The prayers resumed.

All these stories share a common thread. We seem to have fixed mental images of what a spiritual person looks like. Our expectations are held very high and when the chosen figure doesn't live up to our ideals, we're disappointed and disillusioned. These mental images are usually very strident, with little wiggle room. How strict we are! And so the thought occurs to me, hey, it's only a cup of coffee or a chicken leg or a bronze statue.

When my students asked me if it's okay for a yogi to drink coffee, I had to chuckle. And my response was, yeah, if she wants to drink coffee, I think that's okay. As long as she can sit in front of her students with the Starbucks cup and say yes, I drink coffee. If she tries to hide the fact that she's a coffee hound, if she misrepresents who she is, then that's a breech in integrity and that's a little sketchy. Or if she drinks ten cups a day, then that's excessive. If the monks try to hide their drumsticks under their napkins and sneak bites before anyone sees, that's questionable. If they gorge on a 20-piece bucket of extra crispy, that's excessive. I'm thinking we need to soften up some of those hard edges. How about the Middle Way? Equanimity?

Pema Chödrön, Buddhist nun and prolific writer, says that equanimity is thinking bigger than right and wrong. If we can catch our mind hardening into fixed views and soften them, then we can move from being limited to being limitless. Honesty and humor are far more inspiring and helpful than any kind of religious striving for or against anything. When we hold extreme views, there's no room for evolution. Or compassion. Or understanding. Or movement of any kind. When the teacher is pointing to the moon to give the lesson, don't get caught up in looking at the pointing finger. Keep looking for the moon!

So the next time we get all worked up over some perceived indiscretion on the part of our teacher/partner/friend, maybe we can take a moment and remember equanimity, the middle way. Perhaps our hard-edged notions can begin to soften a bit, leaving some room for acceptance. And then, to go even a step further, maybe we can apply the same softening to ourselves. Our rigid idea of who and what we are can begin to smudge a bit, allowing for that freedom of wiggle room.

One of my favorite moments in yoga class is when a student has been striving for a long time to achieve a challenging pose, usually headstand or handstand. And then one day, eureka! The student gets the pose. And suddenly she realizes that a boundary has been erased. And if she's told herself that she could never do headstand, and there she is doing it, then what does that mean about all the other things in life that she's convinced she cannot do? That infernal list of "what I do" and "what I don't do" gets all jumbled up. How wonderful. How liberating.

So, let's get out the erasers and start to erase those thick, dark boundary lines that we've drawn around ourselves and others. Yoga is calling upon us to steer clear of those extreme views that lock us into a fixed, frozen position. Melt that rock-hard view and gently allow your perceptions to open a bit.

…Aaaaaah…

Moments of Moksha

Free at last! Free at last!
Thank God Almighty, I'm free at last!
Martin Luther King, Jr.

Several years back, I was invited to a very hip, über-
cool party of the yoga elite in my stomping grounds
of Dallas, Texas. The invitation read: *Come Celebrate
Randy's Moksha!* Randy's Moksha? Is it like a Bar
Mitzvah? A psychic healing? Vasectomy reversal?
Should I bring a covered-dish casserole? I was hastily
informed that Randy was retiring after a lifetime career
with the FDIC and *moksha* is the Sanskrit word for
freedom. (I saved my Frito Pie for another party.)

Moksha (*mowk*-shuh) translates as freedom, liberation, emancipation. Freedom from the bondage
of attachment. Liberation from delusional thinking.
Emancipation from the prison of our opinions. Since
learning this excellent word, I've become intimate with
its meaning.

There's the obvious physical expression of moksha.
Like liberating yourself from the no-longer-useful-

or-necessary contents of a closet or garage. Emanci-
pating the betamax video of your first wedding. Or
just generally freeing yourself from all the annoying
crap that you've managed to accumulate. Anyone
who's donated to their local thrift store knows the deep
satisfaction of ridding yourself of *all that stuff*. It's like
magic. And after some practice at the base level, cultivating an appreciation for this lightness of being, I had a
supreme opportunity to practice the more subtle aspects
of moksha.

It's been about three years since The Big Disappointment which ultimately led to my Great Moksha. Back
story: While stomping around Dallas, I became deeply
immersed and committed to the Iyengar yoga system.

The Iyengar system has the most rigorous teacher
certification curriculum of all yoga styles and as a
teacher at the Iyengar Studio of Dallas, I was expected
to become certified. This accomplishment requires years
of study and dedication – unlike the bogus courses that
any gym teacher can attend to become a "certified" yogi
in a weekend. (Don't get me started.) I attended class
faithfully under the constant supervision of my teacher
and mentor. I passed the first round of testing and was
well on my way to becoming a Big Shot Yoga Teacher.

But then came a pesky divorce and relocation. I lost
my mentor and consistency of study. Months later,
when I applied for the next level of certification, I was
told that I was unacceptable. I wasn't even allowed
to attempt the test and miserably fail on my own. (In
hindsight, I don't think I received this disturbing news as
gracefully as I could have. Ahem.)

Eventually, this smack became a dynamic catalyst for some juicy self-study. After recovering from the initial shock of my humiliating inadequacy, I pondered my motives to continue along the certification path. Was it still necessary? Do my T-Town students care? Do I? After 15 years of studying the exacting Iyengar system, I concluded I have a good, solid foundation of knowledge and experience. I'm a well-trained instructor and I trust myself as a teacher. Certification Shmertification. I'm headed to Mokshatown!!

To celebrate this epiphany, I created a token of my own appreciation: a *Certificate of Liberation from Certificates*. It reads: "Shanan is hereby free to acknowledge the deep wisdom within which requires no diploma. Encouragement to cultivate and share her own keen insight, unique perspective and sparkling intellect towards her heart's longing is hereby granted. No paperwork required." (I particularly like the "sparkling intellect" part.) The certificate is awarded from Moksha University. Class of 2008.

I realized that the whole certification thing had become so deeply ingrained in my consciousness that I had forgotten it was a choice. And it was now time to choose differently. Of course I will continue to train and study, but my objective is no longer that elusive piece of paper. I've been emancipated from the prison of my own opinions. MOKSHA!

These days, when I find myself in the midst of another mental prison break, I imagine myself thrusting my fist in the air and doing some fancy aerial kickboxing trick while roaring MOKSHA! at the top of my lungs. Like a cosmic super hero. *Look! Up in the sky! It's a bird. It's a plane. It's the Mighty Mistress of Moksha!*

Now all I need is a cape and some groovy magic boots. Would a tiara be too much?

Great Scot! Compassion!

Compassion is the basis of all morality.
Arthur Schopenhauer

Iranian shoe thrower (at Dubya) released early due to
good behavior. Throngs of California inmates released
early due to overcrowding and slashed budgets.
Lockerbie bomber released early due to Scottish com-
passion. Wait. What?

So how about those Scots releasing the Lockerbie
bomber Abdel Baset al-Megrahi? Who knew the Scottish
were so compassionate? There are a few things I think
of as Scottish: whiskey, little black dogs, tartan plaids,
haggis, kilts, Nessie, bagpipes, even Scotch tape, although
I'm not exactly sure about that last one. But compassion?
And even more shocking, compassion as it relates to
justice and the legal/penal system? Holy Sean Connery!

Compassionate release is an established feature of
the British and Scottish judicial systems when a pris-
oner is near death. According to officials, there have
been 30 requests for release on compassionate grounds
in Scotland over the last decade, 23 of which were

approved. (I'm thinking that's probably about half the number of prisoners that were put to death in Texas last week. Clearly the Scots haven't been taught the ways of *compassionate conservatism*.)

Al-Megrahi, a former Libyan intelligence agent, is the only person convicted of the 1988 bombing of Pan Am Flight 103 over the Scottish town of Lockerbie which killed all 259 people on the plane, most of them American, and 11 people on the ground. He was recently given only months to live after being diagnosed with advanced prostate cancer. During the eight years he has served, he has always proclaimed his innocence. Libya didn't formally admit to planting the bomb, yet the Qaddafi regime has paid $2.7 billion in restitution to the victims' families. When al-Megrahi returned to Tripoli, he was celebrated as a national icon.

In granting the release, Scottish Justice Secretary Kenny MacAskill said, "Some hurts can never heal, some scars can never fade. Those who have been bereaved cannot be expected to forget, let alone forgive. However, Mr. al-Megrahi now faces a sentence imposed by a higher power." I like leaving it to the higher power. Maybe the vindictive, ever-judging angry Santa higher power will "impose a sentence" to quench its insatiable thirst for revenge. Or how about the higher power of karma? Hey, we reap what we sow and he's just sown a deeply crappy future for himself. For lifetimes to come. Either way, the guy is screwed. Is that comforting?

Al-Megrahi's conviction was largely based on a shopkeeper who identified him as having bought a shirt in his store in Malta. Scraps of the garment were found wrapped around a timing device discovered in the wreckage. Critics of al-Megrahi's conviction question the reliability of the evidence. In a statement following his release, al-Megrahi protested his innocence. "I say in the clearest possible terms, which I hope every person in every land will hear – all of this I have had to endure for something that I did not do."

(FYI, rumor has it that his release was not based purely on compassion. There's some scuttlebutt that Libyan oil greased the wheels of compassion for the Scottish court. I know. Unbelievable.)

So, is he the evil perpetrator of the deadliest terrorist attack in British history, or a sick old man, a loving father and grandfather, who has suffered a terrible miscarriage of justice? And if we're going to talk about real, true, genuine compassion, does it matter whether he's guilty or not? Mr. Webster defines compassion as the *sympathetic consciousness of others' distress together with a desire to alleviate it.*

It's easy to feel compassion for people I love or those I feel have been treated unjustly. Can I develop compassion for someone who's less lovable to me? Like, say, Dick Cheney? Or Michael Vick? I don't think it's supposed to be *selective compassion.* It's compassion for all. That's the whole point.

Many families of the Lockerbie tragedy voiced their deep anger at the release. Others stated that they've made peace with the incident and do not care. One father, having lost a daughter, believes in al-Megrahi's innocence and encouraged the release. All are under-standable responses. I wonder, if I'd lost a family member to this tragedy, how would I respond?

Britain, meanwhile, scrapped a trade visit to Libya by Prince Andrew amid controversy over the release. Yeah, there's still some work to do. Somebody get Sean Connery on the phone.

Nightmare on St. Valentine's Street: Humorous personal anecdote #47

Oh Lord, it's hard to be humble
when you're perfect in every way
Mac Davis

In 2004, I left my life in California and moved to Texas to marry my longtime, long-distance boyfriend, Gerry. We had a glorious 18 months of marital bliss before the whole thing went right down the tubes and in 2006, I found myself driving from Dallas back to LA on a journey that I often refer to as my Trail of Tears.

It was a difficult split and hearts were hurting. But Time, in its wisdom, heals all things and I was back on the mend as February rolled around. February with its horrific Valentine's Day. In my humble opinion, Valentine's Day can be tricky enough when you *have* a significant other, but when you *don't* have a significant other, Valentine's Day can be brutal.

That being said, I was feeling really good about being single and independent and pretty darn satisfied with my prissy little self. About a week before the Big Day, a local florist called to get my address for an upcoming delivery. Their Texan client wanted to remain anonymous. I gave a long sigh, thanked them, and hung up. Damn him, I thought. Enough already. Can't he just get over it? How pathetic he is! Pitiful, really. But then again, I reminded myself that I'm just so amazingly awesome, it's understandable he would have such a difficult time with our dissolution. Bless his heart. Poor thing.

After a wretched week of foreboding and dread, the Day came. And sure enough, I received a stunningly beautiful bouquet of flowers. I slowly drew the card from its envelope. Inside were the words that sent me reeling: "Love, Astrid." I read the card again. "Love, Astrid." I only wish I could have seen my own face as I realized that the flowers were *not* from my almost ex-husband, they were from a very sweet and generous girlfriend who also lives in Dallas.

I grinned at first. And then the grin turned to smile to chuckle to laugh to guffaw to snortling throat spasms of laughter. I fell to my knees and rolled around clutching my belly, roaring, hooting, chortling. All my self-imposed dread, fear and anxiety instantly disappeared. And all that was left was *my own super-sized, gigantic, massive, gargantuan ego.*

OMG! The good news was that I gave myself the best laugh that I'd had in a long, long time. The bad news was that my overactive mind had conjured up such a dramatic diorama of the Almost Ex: fetal position, thumb in mouth, completely withdrawn from any kind of social interaction. I was to later learn that my Almost Ex was not even close to my deeply disturbed delusion. Uh, no. He was in Vegas with his hot new girlfriend, spinning the roulette wheel and lighting cigars with some of the $300,000 that he'd just inherited from his departed aunt. (Insert snarky comment here.)

As always, the question of the hour is, what does all this have to do with yoga? Firstly, how about a little self-awareness? Self-study is one of the basic tenets of any yoga practice. How do I behave and why? What sets me off? What makes me want to dive down into the rabbit hole??

Behold what amazing scenes I can create with my mischievous mind to make the ego feel important! Then watch as I get righteous and offended over my imagined circumstances, which have absolutely no basis in reality. And then comes the suffering. Suffering that is *completely self-induced.* At any point during that crazy, imagined Valentine's horror, I could have caught myself mid-spin. I could have woken up. I could have snapped out of it. But nooooooo. I'd much rather make myself bug-eyed crazy for a week and then fall into hysterical laughter at my own folly.

And that's another important point. Laughing at our own folly. To my mind, laughter, especially at ourselves, is critical to healing any situation. Make laughter a priority.

So, use my Personal Anecdote #47 as a lesson. Practice self-awareness. Practice laughing. If you can catch yourself at that small window of opportunity before you go careening down into the rabbit hole, you can choose whether to continue down to visit the March Hare or snap out of it and get on with your life.

The brilliant Buddhist nun Pema Chödrön uses a wonderful slogan, "Drop it!" Your mind created it and your mind can drop it. Right now. Without any hesitation. Just like it was a big old hot potato, drop that damaging thought.

But if you do happen to find yourself sipping tea with the March Hare, give him my regards. He knows me well... ;)

Roll up! Roll up
for the Mystery Tour!

Living is easy with eyes closed
Misunderstanding all you see
Lennon/McCartney

In the *Sutra of One Hundred Parables*, the Buddha tells
the story of a young merchant and his son. One day,
the son was kidnapped by a gang of bandits, who razed
the entire village before fleeing. When the merchant
returned home, he found the charred remains of a child
near where his house had been, and in his suffering and
confusion, mistook the charred remains for his own son.
He cried unceasingly, arranged a cremation ceremony,
and then carried the bag of ashes with him day and
night, tied around his neck.

A few months later, his boy escaped from the bandits
and found his way home. When he knocked on the door
of his father's rebuilt house, the father, thinking that
some mischievous boy was ridiculing him, refused to
open the door. The boy knocked and knocked, but the

merchant clung to his view that his boy was dead, and eventually his son had to go away.

The wisdom of the story is apparent. When we vehemently cling to our views or opinions, even if the Truth comes knocking at our door, we will refuse to let it in.

As I slept soundly one night several months ago, my car was invaded and given a good, thorough ravishing. My beloved music was stolen. Yogashanan's Greatest Hits, all taken! Although I have a small music collection at home, my car was where I kept the really good stash. I mourned the loss of my beloved music and tried to practice non-attachment to my tunes. Alas, my practice did not quite hit the target, as you will see. (I bet somehow you predicted that.)

Just yesterday, I completed co-hosting a Women's Weekend Retreat. It required many hours of planning and conspiring with my co-horts in crime to weave together a meaningful and fun experience for our fellow female humans. I cleverly named the event the Magic Mysterical Tour (*mysterical* being a new and brilliant term coined by a wordsmith friend).

My deep wish was to blast the Beatles classic at the beginning of each class. Sadly, I knew that I no longer had this favorite CD because it had been so cruelly *stolen from my car*. My brilliant and capable partner assured me that she could find some version of the song in cyberspace since the Beatles' recordings are not available on iTunes. (And by the way, what's up with that?) After hours of searching, she presented three different versions. We settled on the Cheap Trick variation (yes, Cheap Trick) and blasted the song as the overture to the workshop.

On Sunday evening, as the last yogi departed, my partner and I were ecstatic, exhilarated and exhausted. I decided we must celebrate with the 4th movement of Beethoven's 9th. I ran to my home CD collection, and there, sitting on top of the stack, was Magical Mystery Tour. Right on top. Grinning its evil little grin. Mocking me.

Wait. No. Really? It's been sitting here this whole time? Even as my dedicated partner had spent hours searching, searching, searching for a substitute because I was so sure that thieves had stolen my treasured copy? I felt as if I had my own little bag of ashes tied around my neck. My bag of ashes was the story of my stolen music.

Now, clearly, a dead child and a Beatles CD are two very diverse objects, but the concept is the same. In being rigid in my belief, I imposed an unnecessary load of work on my partner, who was already carrying a full load. Although I had managed to overcome the attachment to my tunes themselves, I'd forged a new attachment to my sad, sad story of being so callously ripped off. If I had taken a moment to look, I could have easily seen that unmistakable album cover. But noooooooo. The truth came knocking at my door and I didn't recognize it. Not only did I not recognize it, I didn't even hear the doorbell ring.

Roll up... Roll up for the Mystery Tour...

Notes on flip-flopping

Change is inevitable.
Except from a vending machine...
Robert C. Gallagher

As a politically astute citizen, I'm a really good yoga instructor. Don't get me wrong, I care greatly about my country. I vote. And I certainly have strong feelings about certain issues. I've always felt that the way I live my life is my political statement. However, my brilliant boyfriend is all about the political scene, so I've recently become more familiar with that nutty, kooky world.

What a bunch of knuckleheads. Many of the political ways are strange to me, but I am particularly mystified by the concept of "flip-flopping." In my limited under-standing, flip-flopping means to change an established opinion on an issue. And the spin doctors tell me that it's a very, very bad thing. It shows a lack of courage, fortitude and determination. We, as the constituency, absolutely do *not* want to have a flip-flopper as a leader. Or friend. Or family member. Or neighbor. Or hall monitor, for that matter.

Well, I don't get it. To me, if a situation changes, or if new information on an issue becomes available, doesn't the wise person consider that? Just suppose that after 15 years of being vegetarian, I get diagnosed with some horrid disease that only a fleshy, beefy diet would cure. Next thing ya know, I'm eating big dripping plates of bacon with bologna chasers. Does that make me a flip-flopper? Am I showing a lack of courage, fortitude and determination? Is someone who quits smoking a flip-flopper?

The scarier idea to me is the "stay the course no matter what" attitude. What if the course becomes dangerous? Or irresponsible? So in the earlier scenario as a vegetarian diagnosed with the horrid meat-hungry disease, if I were running for public office, I'd have to stay the course as vegetarian and just die because otherwise I'd be on the cover of *Newsweek* magazine swilling down my bacon/bologna feast with giant letters screaming *Yogashanan Flip-Flops on Vegetarian Issue! Can She Be Trusted?*

From a yogic perspective, flip-flopping seems a bit like equanimity and flexibility. Being able to go with the flow. Not being so deeply, treacherously attached to an idea or concept. Listening to all sides and learning and evolving when needed. Staying the course *no matter what* seems rigid and unyielding. Forced. And as any yoga practitioner knows, force leads to injury.

And, honestly, when did changing your mind/opinion/ perspective about something become such an unpardonable action? Truth is, we do it constantly. We're relentlessly taking in information and processing it to fit into our own worldview. When some new idea rattles our comfortable little view, we are challenged. Suddenly, there's this new threat to our very neat, organized concept of the world and what is right and what is wrong.

In an open, equitable mind, the new data can be weighed, pondered and then integrated. This is wisdom. And wisdom might tell the committed vegetarian that eating a slab of ribs every now and then could be better for overall health. So you weigh, ponder and integrate. The rigid mind cannot allow this consideration. There is no room for change, evolution. The rigid mind tells the committed vegetarian that ingesting any kind of creature is wrong. Zero tolerance. No wiggle room. Stay the course. So we get one more dead vegetarian from the horrible meat-hungry disease. (FYI, I am a committed vegetarian which is why I can use this snarky analogy.)

Which brings another question to my inquiring mind. What makes us different from all the other creatures on the planet? (Other than the opposable thumb thing.) Isn't one of the biggies our ability to reason and choose? So why, then, is it considered so undesirable to actually use those faculties? When did intellectual flexibility become a liability?

So, sticking with what I know, I retreat back to my yoga practice when overwhelmed by the whole political quagmire. Shunning the political media, I roll out my yoga mat and begin to practice a few forward bends. Or maybe I should work on my twists. No, better yet, I could really use some more back bending. And before I know it, I find myself standing on my head. Flip. Flop. Flip. Flop. Ah, the sound of flexibility…

Trust no one

*You must trust and believe in people
or life becomes impossible.*
Anton Chekhov

While making the drive to Bakersfield recently, I had to
stop at the tracks for a passing train. Among the other
vehicles stopped were about 25 bikers, motorcycles, that
is. (I'm hesitant to say it was a "gang" of bikers. The
word "gang" has such unattractive implications. After
all, I have a good buddy that's a biker dude, and I've
learned that although these guys may look a bit omi-
nous, many of them are just big sweet teddy bears. And
then again, some of them would just as soon rip your
tongue out as look at you. But, hey, this is America, and
that's what makes this country great.)

One particular dude, resplendent in black leather and
wild, wiry facial hair, was stopped very close to my car
and as he turned his head my way, he revealed a pair of
deep brown eyes. I was admiring the somewhat roman-
tic weathering of his face when I caught a glimpse of the
sticker across the front of his helmet: *Trust No One.*

It was a bit of a shock. Heart-breaking really. I mean, damn. That's kind of rough. Trust No One. Not just people over 30, as we were once warned by Tim Leary (or was it Ken Kesey?) and his cohorts. This was very specific. *Trust No One.* The sticker became a springboard of intrigue.

Now clearly, as we make our way through this world, one must learn to temper the Trusting Mind with Wisdom and Discernment. We can't be completely naive. But what happened in this man's life to motivate him to wear this sticker right on the front of his face?? What horrible betrayals did he endure? It's not like it's written on a small button pinned on some discreet place, perhaps within the folds of his well-worn bandana. It screams at you from the front of his helmet. You can't look at the guy without seeing this important message. Like a warning.

If you look up *trust* in Webster's book, you'll find: "Reliance or confidence in someone's good qualities; hope for the future; to allow somebody to do or use something in confidence that the person will behave responsibly or properly," to name a few. Trust implies confidence, faith, reliance and assurance. I believe in you. I know you can do it. Atta boy. You go, girlfriend. The Universe is a friendly place.

What is life like for someone who trusts no one and wears stickers urging others to do the same? Trust No One implies and teaches separation. It's Me vs. You. I cannot rely on you. You are different from me and are not to be trusted with my well-being. And don't trust me to take care of you, either. Brother's keeper, shmother's keeper. But, wait, if I trust no one, then do I trust myself?

What does yoga say to the distrustful biker? A critical question is: Can the distrustful biker be inspired to think otherwise? Could some random act of kindness motivate a shift in his perception? He wasn't born thinking he could trust no one. Something taught him that. So couldn't it be untaught? Relearned? Reconsidered? Yoga says Yes and so did Albert Schweitzer: "Constant kindness can accomplish much. As the sun makes ice melt, kindness causes misunderstanding, *mistrust* and hostility to evaporate."

When the precepts of yoga are practiced with any amount of effort, then trust will be a natural result. When the idea of Union is contemplated (yoga translates as "union"), we begin to recognize that you and I are really the same. We ultimately want the same things. We all want happiness, peace and understanding. We all want to be able to trust and be trusted.

So I've prepared my own set of forehead stickers for the next time I see my biker dude. As I wait for the train to make its way past us, I'm going to whip out my own freshly minted box of *Yogashanan's 4Heads 4Peace: Spreading the Love One Frontal Cortex at a Time*. This particular box includes:

> "One must be fond of people and trust them if one is not to make a mess of life."

> "To be trusted is a greater compliment than to be loved."

"You can't shake hands with a closed fist."

And my personal favorite:

> *"What if the hokey-pokey really is what it's all about???"*

Think about it.

The sacred art
of shutting up

If you keep your mouth shut,
you will never put your foot in it.

Austin O'Malley

I don't remember where I first heard this particular bit
of wisdom, but it's become a real favorite. I've tried to
live by its high standard and I can't say I've always succeeded. I've passed it on to many friends and students
and now I want to share with you this great universal
precept. You can file it right along with other pithy
insights like *Whoever is happy will make others happy,*
too or *What goes around comes around* or *The best*
things in life are free or *Do unto others as you would*
have them do unto you. Today, I offer for your consideration: **Never miss a good opportunity to shut up.**

I cannot overemphasize the benefit of this practice.
Learning to shut up has been a tremendous vehicle for
self-study. In observing my mental activity during any
given day, I make these startling discoveries:

OPPORTUNITY #1: **I have the strong urge to butt in while someone else is talking**

Why is it that when someone else is relaying their story to me, I get the overwhelming desire to interrupt them with my opinion or comment? Sometimes I don't even hear what they're saying, I only know that my commentary is of cosmic worth and if only they'd just let me get a word in edgewise they could experience the depths of my wisdom. Or sometimes I believe that I can express their own idea so much more skillfully than they can. I'm so busy formulating what I'm going to say that I don't really hear what my companion is saying.

OPPORTUNITY #2: **I have the strong urge to top a friend's story**

As you're telling me about your adventure, your thrill or your proud achievement, I'm scanning my own databanks for similar experiences. Only better. Your son won the What I Did on My Summer Vacation essay contest at school? That's cute. Did I ever mention my daughter was named Most Perfect/Popular/Beautiful by her school and the entire school district?

OPPORTUNITY #3: **When someone is suffering**

When someone is sharing their troubles, I am tempted to fix it. Tell them it's all going to be okay, which is hogwash because if I've learned anything in my time on this planet, I know that it's *not* always going to be okay. Hurt happens. And then I may throw in the topper (see #2 above): Your house is in foreclosure? Gee, that's tough. Did you know that once my house burned to the ground destroying all our worldly possessions?

OPPORTUNITY #4: **When I find myself finishing someone else's sentences**

OMG, this is really, really bad, amazingly rude and irritating. My mom always used to finish my dad's sentences
and it would completely unnerve him. Not surprisingly, I
am equally horrified to find myself doing the same thing.

EXTRA CREDIT: **When I'm relentlessly haranguing
myself**

After some time of training in shutting up with others,
and enjoying the remarkable benefits of the practice, it
dawned on me that I could apply the same technique to
my own inner dialogue. As I was very busy condemning
myself over some misdeed one day, I thought, hey! Never
miss a good opportunity to shut up *especially to myself.*
How about quieting that snarky critic living in my
head? If I can learn to restrain my ego-talk as someone
is telling me how sweet her boyfriend is (when I know
mine is infinitely sweeter!), then surely I can make the
mindful shift to silence my own screeching inner harpy.

As a student of yoga, I keep in mind that yoga teaches
non-violence, including cutting into someone's story
or slamming myself for some perceived mistake. *Non-
hoarding,* even of the drive and scope of a conversation.
Non-stealing, even of another person's freedom to finish
a sentence. So I practice the sacred art of shutting up.
I remind myself to dial down my own need to speak
and instead, deeply listen to the other person. Quiet
myself and pay attention to others. It's a beautiful and
humbling practice. And the opportunities, seriously, are
endless. Now get out there and shut the hell up.

Yoga as GPS

No matter where you go, there you are.
Confucius

My brilliant 25-year-old son, the video game developer, has his dream job with an independent gaming company in LA. He makes great money, is in a position to actually create his own games and works the ideal gamer hours of 11am-ish to 8pm-ish or whenever he can manage to make it in. He and his fellow gaming geeks eat sushi for lunch and drink Red Bull or Rock Star and just generally live the 25-Year-Old Boy Utopia.

Now don't get me wrong, he's no slacker. He works hard, is responsible for million-dollar game designs and has busted his butt to get to where he is today. He holds a degree in Video Imaging and relentlessly hounded the gaming industry Big Dogs to land this perfect gig.

That being said, one of his first purchases with his newfound wealth was a portable GPS system. Not only can he mount it in his Hyundai, but he can take it into Hollywood to find his way to the nearest Amoeba Music or Game Stop or Brazilian meatfest restaurant.

When he showed me his new toy, I was appropriately impressed. At the same time, I thought it a bit frivolous, but hey, the Boy is making his own money and can spend $300 on an electronic gadget if he likes, right? And as he explained to me, "Mom, I'm like Einstein. I can understand and even explain to you String Theory, but I can't find my way home." Right. And this thing is his most treasured possession – well, besides the Roomba, iPod, DS and a couple of other e-items that I really have no clue as to what they do.

But that being said, this GPS thing is really very cool, and it struck me how simple and direct and beautiful this little piece of equipment really is. In fact, it's even a bit yogic.

The GPS system asks only two questions: Where are you now? and Where do you want to go? It doesn't care where you've been or what your history is. It doesn't care if your car is a shiny new Beamer or a battered old Buick. GPS stays completely present moment. (And it will even guide you in the accent of your choice. My son prefers the Australian.)

But the best part, if you somehow do not follow the directions properly, if you're not listening or get distracted or just completely disregard it while you're taking a sip of your Red Bull, it will recalculate for you and start you off in the right direction again. No scolding. No judgment.

The more I got to know this little electronic helper, the more I began to see the metaphysical implications. OMG – yoga is like a transcendental GPS system! A guide to where you want to go. Yoga asks, "Where's your mind now?" and then "Where would you like it to be?" or "Where is your hip flexor now?" and "Where would you like it to be?" And then gives an impartial, non-judgmental guide on how to get there.

If you don't follow the directions properly, are not listening or get distracted while sipping your chamomile tea, it will simply get you back on track.

"Where are you now?"

"I'm at 1522 Misery Lane, three blocks west of Unsatisfied Street."

"Where do you want to go?"

"To the nearest Enlighten-Mart, intersection of Contentment and Happiness."

"Got it." (Imagine the Australian accent.) "Proceed down Self-Study Street towards Understanding Ave. Turn right. Go five miles to Compassion Circle and turn left."

"Oops. I've taken a wrong turn at Desire Ave! I'm at a deadend on Ego Blvd."

"No problem. I'll recalculate...... okay. U-turn out of Ego Blvd back towards Compassion Circle, passing Equanimity and Truthfulness. Merge onto the Interstretch Hwy and then follow Truthfulness to the signal at Kindness Lane and veer right towards Middle Way. Three blocks to the Enlighten-Mart at corner of Contentment and Happiness. Turn left into parking lot and sit quietly. You have arrived."

"Thanks, GPS."

"I'm here to point the way. Have a nice day!"

(You can only imagine the look on the face of my 25-year-old Einstein as I relayed my analogy to him. He just couldn't roll his eyes far enough. "Yeah, okay, whatever, Mom. Hey, did I tell you I solved Rubik's cube in 47 seconds? I'm designing my own now.")

I love the concept of yoga as your own personal navigation method. Rather than a Global Positioning System, think of it as a Peace of Mind Positioning System. A guide. A pointer. A navigator. So, consider: Where are you now? Where do you want to go? Time to refresh your map? Need an impartial, non-judgmental, neutral guide to show the way? Try the Peace of Mind Positioning System – also known as Yoga.

Hey, even Einstein needed an occasional direction or two.

The Hoover Sutra

The greatest mistake you can make in life
is to be continually fearing you will make one.
Elbert Hubbard

When I first began yoga way back in the last century, a group of us decided to attend a Big La-Tee-Dah Yoga Workshop being taught by a Big La-Tee-Dah Yoga Instructor. We were initially very excited as we signed up and paid the big bucks. But as the date approached, our excitement turned to deep anxiety.

We were new to this yoga thing and not terribly experienced. Would we be good enough? What if they did some poses that I've never done? Headstand!? Handstand!? What would the other students think if I were to crash to the floor? Could we manage to complete the sessions without humiliating ourselves? How can I navigate this dangerous, deadly yoga workshop night-mare without losing the last few shreds of self-esteem that I have? We can't do this! I want my money back!!

Aaaah, the sweet taste of complete and utter panic. I realized I was spinning out of control from the terror of not being good enough or smart enough or thin enough or whatever enough. Even back then, I understood that a disturbed mind would be a distinct obstacle if I wanted to actually *learn* something from a world-class teacher. If I'm so caught up in how I'm appearing to others, I'll lose the capacity to truly listen and study.

I needed a new mindset, a new perspective. As Einstein once said: *A problem cannot be solved from the same consciousness that created it.* And with that in mind, I made a mental shift and a dazzling new philosophy was born.

Instead of the typical fretting over being the smartest one in the room, or the funniest, or the most successful, I went in an all-new direction. And thus, these words of wisdom were coined: *There's a very real possibility that I may be the suckiest one in the room. And I'm okay with that.*

My Suckiest-One-in-the-Room Philosophy was a big hit with my yoga buds. We had a laugh and I discovered a new, refreshing perspective. When I abandon the tendency to judge myself or compare myself to others, I can relax. When I take my ego out of the equation, anxiety dissolves and I am free from the incessant drone of my insecurity. I'm just showing up with all the other yogis and rolling out my mat and doing the best I can at this point in time. If I have the crappiest pose in the room, well, that's okay with me. Do I suck? You bet I do! Thanks for noticing! Namaste!

This revelatory concept, later known as the Hoover Sutra, has been invoked on many occasions since that first fateful workshop. (As it happened, we all survived nicely and developed major crushes on Rodney Yee, Yogi Stud of the Universe. He even called me by name and whispered in my ear to soften my hyper extending elbows in Downward Dog. I almost collapsed with ecstasy.) When I traveled to India in 2004 to study with the Iyengar family, there were close to 500 students in the ginormous hall and I was obediently sucking right in the front row.

I realize that one must be mindful to avoid Hoover Sutra abuse. I don't want to become so comfortable in the Suckiest One role that I neglect to grow or improve. By the same token, I don't want to effort so hard that I snap a hamstring to compete with my Gumby neighbor. Balancing the fine line between the yoga philosophical tenets of Effort (tapas) and Contentment (santosha) is a subtle and intriguing practice. Too much Effort leads to egoism and injury. Too much Contentment leads to dullness and stagnation.

So practice the wisdom of Yogashanan's Hoover Sutra with discernment! When you notice you're comparing and demeaning yourself with all your perceived inadequacies, try adjusting your consciousness to consider the delight of being the Suckiest One. Lighten up. Have a gentle laugh at your sense of self-importance and accept where you are in this moment in time. With the companions of Effort and Contentment by your side, establish your own best practice.

And if anyone says you suck, thank them. And feel free to quote the Hoover Sutra.

Notes on Iyengar instruction

*As a teacher, if you cannot work on yourself
in your practice then you will not be able
to get others to work on themselves.*

BKS Iyengar

I am a yoga instructor. To be more precise, I'm an
Iyengar yoga instructor.

(The name Iyengar is taken from BKS Iyengar, the
gentleman who developed this particular technique and
is still alive and kicking and back bending and twisting
and standing on his head at the ripe old age of eighty-
something in Pune, India.)

Anyone who has investigated the different schools
of yoga soon finds that each school has its own unique
approach and the Iyengar school is certainly no excep-
tion. A typical Iyengar-style instruction would be,
"Stretch your arms straight up. Now, keeping the arms
extending upwards, draw the shoulder blades down the
back..." or "Lift the chest... Now, maintaining a lifted
chest, twist your trunk to the left."

It's the idea of maintaining one action while adding
another action. Can you perform both actions at the

same time? Doing one thing, can you add another thing and then work them both equally, thus developing a sense of equanimity in the body? Maintaining A, perform B. Expand your awareness to now include those two actions simultaneously without losing any of A or forcing B.

And then, of course, as your practice develops and becomes more sophisticated, you add even more layers, one upon the other, until the consciousness is evenly spread throughout the body and the effort becomes effortless. Right.

I have recently had the profound opportunity of observing this "maintaining A, perform B" concept in my personal life. The past few years have been very kind to me. I do what I love. I have good, healthy relationships with friends and family. I have a beautiful home in an idyllic mountain hamlet. I'm healthy, I'm happy, I'm good to go.

In my delight, I wondered aloud, "Could it get any better than this?" And then, from out of nowhere, came a booming **YES!** from Life. I fell in love. Deeply, wonderfully, powerfully. And here comes the Iyengar instruction: "Keeping a well-balanced mind, grounded heart and busy, diverse lifestyle, now fall in love." Can I balance my previous actions while adding this new essential action and keep them both equally working?

So far the answer to that question has been a resounding No. I have been completely distracted by my new relationship. My old routine of morning meditation and yoga practice has been abandoned. My mala beads gaze at me longingly. My yoga mat could use a good dusting. To relate back to the Iyengar instruction, I have allowed my chest to collapse while I twisted my waist.

I've let my arms bend while pulling down my shoulder blades. I've abandoned the first action so that I could perform the second action. I've neglected all alignment. Equanimity shmequanimity.

So now my practice becomes expanding my awareness enough to include this new layer in my experience. Can I make that quantum leap? Of course I can. It's similar to when you've had your first baby and then you become pregnant with the second child. You think, "How could I ever love another child as much as Little Tommy?" And then Baby Susie pops out and you gaze into her eyes and your heart just blasts through all previously set boundaries for loving.

And just in case this has all gotten a bit too sticky gooey grossly sweet, I'm reminded that this whole process can also go in the opposite direction. In my deepest despair after my dad's unexpected death and my own gruesome divorce, I wondered aloud, "Could it possibly get any worse?" The next week my house burned down. Not kidding.

So, in Iyengar-style instruction: "Maintaining the agony of losing your dad, and your 12-year marriage dissolving into an ugly smear on the pavement, now watch your home and all your possessions go up in smoke, lost forever. Take that, Miss Prissypants." And in that same feat of quantum leaping, the heart blasts through all the previously set boundaries for suffering.

So be prepared to deal with the answer if you ask the question, "Could it get any better/worse than this?" It can. It does. It will. Boundaries get blown. Love happens. Loss happens. It's the Flow. Riding it *with equanimity* is the practice. Maintaining A, perform B.

Shaken and stirred

Gather ye rosebuds while ye may.
Robert Herrick

Wow. I have been wholly shaken by a recent journalistic piece. I don't know if journalistic is the right word. I do know shaken is the right word. Horrified. Sickened. Disgusted. Appalled. Traumatized. You get the idea. Let the rant begin…

As part of a recent Mother's Day Salute Extravaganza Jubilee Celebration, there was a half-page aditorial devoted to the supposed "latest trend" in mothering. Perhaps you caught the article/ad on *The New Mommy Makeover*? Seems that the typical, old-school Mother's Day Makeover of a relaxing facial and mani/pedi with a cute little jeweled daisy on the big toe has morphed into a menacing demonic incarnation referred to as The New Mommy Makeover. Move over hot stone massage. Move in scalpel and suction.

According to the writer/doctor of the article/ad, who I will refer to as Dr. Youvegottobekiddingme, his office has been deluged with calls begging him to perform The

New Mommy Makeover on countless drab, overworked moms. As I read the article, my eyes and my level of disbelief expanded. Some of my favorite quotes include:

"After childbearing, women want their bodies back."

"Pregnancy is not kind to bodies."

"Stretch marks and hanging breasts. You can't exercise those away."

"The daily grind of caring for children doesn't mix well with rigorous gym schedules."

"Faces get careworn, too, with the exhaustion and frustrations that raising kids can entail."

Wow, doc, forget the boob job. Just hand me the morphine drip.

Two of my personal favorites were included as reasons why so many mothers are now happily and gratefully turning to plastic surgery: "More older mothers these days, their bodies get more out-of-control." That just makes me laugh. "Career women want to look competitive when they exit the Mommy Track." Really? The Mommy Track?

He goes on to say how the trend is here to stay, especially due to "spoiled Boomer women, they won't tolerate a normal post-partum look." What does that mean exactly?

He says one client, a 38-year-old mother of four, "got a tummy tuck, breast lift, liposuction and brow lift. After she was healed, she looked extraordinary." Wait. Define extraordinary.

I hang my head in despair. So let me get this straight, doc. Now that I've had the ultimate sacred experience that my body is designed for. And now that I've

miraculously grown a new Life inside me and given
birth to that Life. And now that I've nursed this
Mini-Me at my happy, bountiful breast and fallen completely in love with this new precious person, well, I'd
better get on with the important business at hand. Get
that prenatal body back. Me and my sagging, dragging
breasts and soft, squashy belly are unattractive, unpleasant and unacceptable!

Time is wasting, girlie. And understand that nutritious food and sensible exercise will never be enough.
After the hideous birth-giving torture that the body has
undergone, well, thank God our offices are here to help
you out of this unfortunate and embarrassing situation
right now. Surgeons are standing by.

So I tear out my hair and stomp my feet and rail
on about how our culture is caught up in the external
appearance of things. I'm heartsick to think that any
young mother (or older mother with her out-of-control
body) would read the piece and judge themselves by
these skewed standards. We have been inundated and
stunned by the relentless hounding message that tells us
we are our appearance. We long to be beautiful because
that's what we've been conditioned to believe will bring
us happiness. And now the evil New Mommy Makeover
and all its ignorant implications. Argh.

So how do I talk myself down from this one? I get it
that I'm very attached to my view on this subject and it's
my strong attachment that is causing my distress. I also
know that I've seen many women/mothers struggle with
impossible body image expectations that cause so much
suffering. Preventable suffering. So yoga, as usual, would

probably teach compassion for Dr. Y and acceptance for the women who are calling to schedule their appointments for their New Mommy Makeovers.

Compassion and Acceptance. Sounds like good ingredients for a Yogi Makeover. And maybe the pedicure with the cute daisy on the big toe.

Notes on integrity

Wise men, though all laws were abolished,
would lead the same lives.

Aristophanes

In his beautiful book, *Fire of Love*, Aadil Palkhivala
relates an illuminating tale about Mahtma Gandhi:

> One day, a distraught mother came to him with her
> rebellious son. She explained that the boy's behavior
> was erratic and troubling, and that this was certainly
> due to the enormous amount of sugar he consumed.
> She pleaded with Gandhi to tell the boy to stop,
> saying, "He won't listen to me, but you are the great
> Mahatma of the nation. He will listen to you." Much
> to the disappointment of the mother, Gandhi immedi-
> ately replied, "Come back and see me in a week."
>
> A week later, the mother and son returned.
> Without any formalities, Gandhi announced to the
> boy, "You must stop eating sugar immediately."
> The mother, much relieved, couldn't hold in her
> curiosity and asked the Mahatma, "Gandhiji, please

forgive me for asking, but why didn't you tell him
that last week?" Gandhiji slowly lifted his head,
looked directly into her eyes, and thoughtfully said,
"First I had to stop eating sugar myself before I
advised your son to do the same."

This story is a direct reflection of Gandhi's deep
commitment to *integrity*. Palkhivala describes integrity
as "when your words and actions match your thoughts
and beliefs. When our words and our actions are severed
from our thoughts and beliefs, an inner, subconscious
stress develops, a pain in our conscience, a disturbance
in our soul. We become disconnected."

Disconnect is the polar opposite of what yoga
teaches. Yoga translates as "union." The aim of a yoga
practice is to unite. It's all about connection, unification.
Unite word and action. Connect thought and deed. Walk
the Talk. A big happy peaceful ball of Oneness.

With this concept in mind, I turn to self-study. I notice
how it is so easy for me to strongly push for my students
to develop a daily practice even while my own daily
practice has diminished. I can easily urge my beloved
boyfriend to ease up on the sugar as I head for the Rite-
Aid ice cream counter. I've chastised my mom for her
Diet Coke habit while holding my third cup of coffee in
my hand. (My charming little personal examples of this
unbalanced, non-integrity style of behavior are endless.
I'll let you think of a few of your own. Seriously.)

Integrity implies wholeness, completeness, coherence.
It also implies a deep level of honesty. Honesty that
moves from the inside out. When I'm behaving in a way

that is in alignment with my heart and mind, I am at peace. If I waver from that alignment, just like in a physical yoga practice, I can get injured. Damaged. To do one thing while saying another causes discomfort on many levels. Dis-ease. Illness. If my actions have no foundation, they have no potency. No effectiveness. No value. No power. No shirt. No shoes. No service. No kidding.

We've all heard Mahatma Gandhi's wise slogan, "Be the change you want to see in the world." How many of us could possibly claim such integrity? Particularly in this highly charged political season! As we rail against the rigidity of the other party's view, we stick steadfastly to our own view. We want them to listen to our side even as we turn a deaf ear to their side. We charge the other team with spreading lies and spinning the truth even as our own party does the same thing. So how do we begin that critical shift towards a more united, compassionate and tolerant society? That big happy peaceful ball of Oneness? Hmmmmmm... Be the change...

So if I want to have a more peaceful and loving nation, I must be a more peaceful and loving individual. If I want my voice to be heard, I must listen to the voices of others. If I want to end the war(s), I must look within to my own war raging in myself. The war of walk vs. talk. The war of reducing my cups of coffee before scolding my mom about her Diet Coke. The war of foregoing my chocolate chip ice cream before reprimanding my own Beloved about his fructose intake.

The battle for integrity that wages in my own mind must be brought under control if I dream of cultivating a society where true integrity is a core value. In keeping with the war analogy, perhaps a "surge" is in order? A powerful push of regular meditation and yoga practice! A new fresh battalion of brave warriors dedicated to eradicating the insurgency of fraudulence, dishonesty and deceit. A company of compassion sent into the war zone of separation and disconnection. Bring it on!!

Maybe then we can truly proclaim, "Mission Accomplished."

Wake up!

In waking a tiger, use a long stick.
Mao tse Tung

Isn't it fascinating how Life has a way of showing you what needs work – what lessons need to be learned. Sometimes Life can be very gentle and whisper softly in your ear, "Hey there, Yogashanan, you're needing a little more attention in this area. Think you could perhaps be a bit more mindful as you're making these decisions?"

And then sometimes it's more like the proverbial frying pan to the face: "Okay, kid, I've given you this hint a gazillion times. Being subtle is not working, so now it's time for a smack right between the eyes." And the last thing you see is the frying pan heading for your mug. Too late to duck. Can't squeeze the toothpaste back into the tube. Just brace yourself for the spank. I recently experienced a brilliant example of this.

I had a few hints that I wasn't being fully present to my life. Things like losing my phone, locking my keys in my car *with the motor running*, wondering aloud if I had clothes on before I walked out the door (which a friend tells me is a really really good clue that I've been living alone far too long), I think you get the picture.

So I'm visiting a dear friend in LA and we are in this lengthy, deep discussion as he'd been lately feeling depressed about what to do with his pathetic excuse for a life and I had been lending a sympathetic ear. After all, he's a good buddy and needed to process a demon or two. After the third or fourth hour, I was desperately trying to conceal my undeniable urge to go screaming out of the room. His despair was relentless.

When our meeting came to a merciful close, I left and walked the short distance to my car which was parked on a side street. Still caught up in the fog of my pal's despondency, I started the car and drove slowly towards a busy intersection. I began mindlessly creeping into traffic when suddenly an enormous SUV came hurtling around the corner, nearly sheering off my left headlight and a very angry man yells out his window, *"Hey! Wake up!"* while giving me a particularly significant finger signal. (Ah, yes, the City of Angels.)

I slammed on my brakes. I sat in stunned silence for a moment and then began to laugh like a lunatic. I realized he was absolutely right and how wonderful that he'd chosen those particular words.: *Wake up!* He could have chosen a million different rude remarks to hurl at me, but he didn't. He shouted, *"Wake Up!"*

I love that. I took it to mean so much more than he'd intended. In fact, as he went screeching past me, I'm sure he thought I was a complete idiot as I chortled away in my goofy little clown car. Wake up, indeed. I wanted to shout back at him "Yes! Yes! Thank you! Thanks for the reminder!" But I knew that would guarantee me a seat at the nuthouse. (And very possibly a gunshot wound to the head. After all, this was LA.) To me, this guy had been the Great Yogi Messenger disguised as a red-faced, pissed off, infuriated urban guerilla citizen. Bless his heart.

Yoga asks us to wake up. Pay attention. Come to. Get going. Activate. Stir up. Light a fire. Get conscious. Snap out of it. So much of the time we walk around as if in a coma, wrapped up in our own small tight little minds. Tunnel vision. Contracted and withdrawn. Yoga says make your mind expansive. Broaden your awareness. Extend. Increase. Open. Lengthen. Stretch. Heighten.

All these are words I use as a yoga teacher when instructing the class in the physical poses of yoga. Extend your arms. Open your chest. Lengthen your hamstrings. Broaden your collarbones. And as we learn to do all these things with the body, we can also learn to do these things with the mind. Open the mind. Broaden the consciousness. Lengthen your awareness. Wake up! (When the Buddha was asked, "Are you a god?" He would only answer, "I am awake." The word buddha means *awakened one*.)

In my bedroom, I have an alarm clock that has three different settings. Alarm One is a softly flashing light, no sound. Ten minutes later Alarm Two is the flashing light accompanied by a loud but resonate chime. Another ten minutes brings Alarm Three with the now-blinding flashing light intermingled with the piercing blast of a deafening siren designed to alert the hounds of hell. One way or the other I'm going to be woken up. It can be soft and quiet or irritating and difficult. My choice.

Life can whisper in my ear or smack me across the face. One way or the other I'm going to be woken up. My choice. Yoga is a tool to help awaken me at Alarm One, the whisper. Yoga gives me a heads up before the frying pan gets to my face. Yoga stretches my hamstrings and my awareness, bringing a freedom that's just too brilliant to ignore.

Now if I could just find that damn phone...

Top ten excuses for not trying yoga

or
How I learned to stop worrying
and downward face my dog

What? Me worry?
Alfred E. Neuman

Body? What body? I have a body?? *(Benefit: increased body awareness)* Most of us live so much in our heads that we forget we're actually walking around in this amazing mechanism called the human body. We've become so deeply disconnected that when asked to stretch the arms or lift the chest, we're completely stumped. It's not uncommon to hear a student ask if her arms are straight because she simply can't distinguish straight from bent in her own body. One of the first perceptible yoga gifts is a heightened physical awareness.

I'm one chocolate bar away from a complete and very ugly meltdown. *(Benefit: stress reduction)* Stress is profoundly destructive and potentially lethal. Yoga practice includes physical movement, breath awareness and conscious relaxation, all proven tamers of the stress dragon. Yoga's effect of lowering levels of hormone neurotransmitters creates a feeling of calm, and research points to a boost in oxytocin, the so-called *trust* and *bonding* hormone that's associated with feeling relaxed and connected to others.

My heart can't take it. *(Benefit: heart health)* One of the most studied areas of the health benefits of yoga is its effect on heart disease. Yoga has long been known to lower blood pressure and slow the heart rate which benefits people with hypertension, heart disease and stroke. (Stress, anyone?) Yoga is a key component of the program designed by Dean Ornish, MD, to reverse heart disease through lifestyle and diet rather than surgery. On the biochemical level, yoga has been associated with decreased cholesterol and triglyceride levels as well as a boost in immune system function.

I have balance problems. *(Benefit: finding equanimity)* Balance issues are challenging. Yoga's attention to a strong and solid foundation is key. When balance is an issue, practicing *asana* (yoga poses) with the support of a wall is very helpful. Developing an acute awareness of the feet coupled with an energetic sense of grounding can go a long way in finding your physical balance point. And, of course, cultivating a balanced *mind* can also be beneficial. Yeah, there's that.

Yoga is for wimps. *(Benefit: physical strength and endurance)* Ha ha ha ha. Most folks who make this proclamation have never attended a yoga class. Yoga can be as challenging as any physical exercise or sport.

Try some deep backbending or standing on your head for 15 minutes and see how wimpy it feels. Yoga develops strength and endurance just as effectively as it develops flexibility and balance.

I'm depressed. *(Benefit: improved mental health)* In a demonstration of personal transparency, this is the reason I sought out yoga: a heavy depression. I felt perceptibly better after my very first session. Nearly every yogi will testify they feel happier and more contented after class, a benefit that may result from yoga's boosting oxygen levels to the brain. Or maybe it's the stretchy pants.

I can't focus. *(Benefit: greater clarity)* Concentration and the ability to mentally focus are common benefits you'll hear from yoga students. As asana practice develops your capacity for focused attention on the body, it can also develop your capacity for focused attention towards life's endless mysteries. Like remembering what it was you were looking for in the refrigerator as you stand there, fridge door open, wondering what it was you were looking for.

I'm too stiff, too old, too fat. *(Benefit: lose the bullsh*t excuses)* I've often begun class by asking if anyone has injuries or other chronic conditions with the stipulation that being old and/or fat doesn't count. This usually gets a giggle of recognition from the students. Truth is, yoga is appropriate for all ages, sizes and levels of (in)flexibility.

My back/shoulders/hips/eyelashes/whatever hurts. *(Benefit: freedom from pain)* By using asana along with meditation and breath work, pain can be managed and minimized. I have been the happy witness to many students relieving chronic pain through their commitment to yoga practice. Don't let pain be your excuse. Let it be your motivation!

I'm afraid to meet Yogashanan. *(Benefit: loads of fun)* Understandable, but don't waste time living in the prison of your fear. Just get your asana to class.

Requiem for a broken mala

*Creativity involves breaking out of established patterns
in order to look at things in a different way.*

Edward de Bono

Mala – Sanskrit for garland; usually refers to a sacred
necklace made of 108 beads and used for meditation; an
Indian-style rosary (which also shares the 108 bead thing).

When I first started this yogic journey many years ago,
some friends gifted me a "Beginner's Yoga Kit" which
included some sacred texts, a few sticks of incense
and a simple sandalwood mala. This mala became my
constant companion and an indispensable part of my
meditation practice.

In the years to come, even as I gave away most of my
belongings to become a yogi gypsy and travel the world,
I always had the mala. It accompanied me through
Italy, Germany, Mexico and halfway across the U.S.
I've imbued it with hundreds of hours of meditation. It
symbolized my spiritual practice. Whenever I felt like
I might need some extra protection, I turned to these

beloved beads with a deep inner confidence. And then, just recently, the unthinkable happened.

My mala broke. No, really, my mala beads broke. I was sitting doing my meditation, passing each bead through my fingers as I chanted away, and suddenly I felt the string of beads crumble in my hands and spill into my lap. Unbelievable. Impossible. The symbol of my spiritual practice broken, crumbled, unstrung, wrecked, kaput. What could this mean? I'm convinced there must be some deeply significant meaning to this incident. But what??

I became obsessed with this disastrous turn of events. I regaled a fellow meditator with my sad tale and she informed me that when your mala breaks, that means you've learned something. You've made a breakthrough. Well, needless to say, I *loved* this concept. Although I had absolutely no idea what I'd learned or what my miraculous breakthrough could be, I really liked the notion that I'd made progress. Ha.

My meditation sessions following this tragic incident seemed hopeless. Something was missing. My mind was even more unruly, undisciplined, unskillful. Without my dear mala, I was lost. Lost? Really? All these years of practice dashed just because I no longer have my beads? Oh. Wait. I'm starting to get it. My precious mala was a tool, to be sure, and that's *all* it was. A tool. An assistant. And here I am losing steam in my practice simply because I've lost my holy gizmo? Have I become so wound up in the prop that I'm now ignoring the Real Practice? Can anyone say "attachment"?

The use of props is a defining and brilliant feature of Iyengar-style yoga asana. If a pose is not manageable in any way, props can lend support to help the student experience the pose. But at some point as your practice progresses, you want to be able to discard the props. I've observed many students continue to use props when they are no longer necessary. I've actually barked at students to get rid of the block, strap, blanket, whatever when I saw that it was hindering their progress. Yeah. I'm getting it alright. (Mirrors, mirrors everywhere and no black curtain to hide behind.)

In the spirit of saving the best part of the story for last: After mourning the loss of my beloved mala and getting a glimpse of my deep attachment to the prop, I gave the precious unstrung beads to an innovative friend who transformed them into an amazing piece of sacred art that now hangs above my altar. She then used the few remaining beads to fashion a necklace that I absolutely adore. Usually I am not one for jewelry, but this necklace has a special mojo that is undeniable. I truly adore both my art piece and my necklace. Creation from destruction. Only my destroyed mala could have provided the raw materials for these two brilliant creations. Such amazing transformation. Can I be equally transformed?

I have since acquired a new mala. I can hardly wait until it breaks.

K-9 compassion in action

*The average dog is a nicer person
than the average person.*

Andy Rooney

In those first raw days as the West Ranch fire was being
fought and we were all losing our minds with worry
and upset, my friend Constance and her trusty canine
companion, Sir Duke, served as an emergency relief
and therapy team. (Sir Duke is a spectacular young
Golden Retriever who also happens to be a Disaster
Stress Relief Dog, trained and certified by Therapy Dogs
International.)

I like to imagine the nourishing kindness shimmering
out of my sweet friend and her beloved Duke as they
brought their own remarkable kind of healing to the
devastating situation. As he lovingly moved through
the crowd, Sir Duke made gentle and persistent offers
of a compassionate head to pet or paw to hold. He
was considered an essential caregiver by the Incident
Command Staff and was ultimately awarded a Medal of
Honor for his valuable contribution. Sir Duke and his

trusty human companion, Constance, had soothed many a broken heart.

Becoming a Disaster Stress Relief Dog is no easy feat. The testing is rigorous and the dog must exhibit a distinctive personality. As I perused the list of required canine behaviors, I wondered to myself in amusement, could *I* pass the therapy dog test? Could you? Consider these requirements for Therapy Dog Certification (aka **walking the bodhisattva's path**):

◇ *Accepting a Friendly Stranger* – Dog *will allow friendly stranger to approach and speak to handler in everyday situation; the dog must show no sign of resentment or shyness (**aka EQUANIMITY**)*
I usually have no problem with my handler speaking to others. However, do I greet friendly strangers with equal enthusiasm? With no sign of resentment or shyness?

◇ *Sitting Politely for Petting* – Dog *will allow friendly stranger to touch it (**aka ACCEPTANCE**)*
Can I listen graciously while others share their heartache with me? Without having to add my own two cents? Accept whatever is expressed, without judgment, while returning only love?

◇ *Walking in Crowd* – Dog *is polite in pedestrian traffic and under control in public places; dog can show interest in strangers without being over-exuberant, shy or resentful (**aka INNER PEACE**)*
I'm polite and am usually able to remain in control in public places. However, over-exuberance could be an issue.

◇ *Sit down/Stay in place – To show dog is trained,*
handler moves away but dog stays in place
(aka HUMILITY/CONTENTMENT)
Can I rest in the deep knowing that everything's
okay? Can I practice non-attachment so I don't
become unbalanced when my best friend leaves
my side?

◇ *Leave It – Handler walks dog within three feet of*
food; upon command, dog must ignore food
(aka PRATYAHARA; Withdrawal of the Senses;
Fourth Limb of Yoga)
I seriously doubt my capacity to maintain focus while
being walked on a loose leash past a big steaming
plate of Petra's garlic fries. The suffering children be
damned. It's Petra's garlic fries.

◇ *Supervised Separation – Evaluator takes dog while*
handler leaves for approximately three minutes; dog
should not show anything stronger than mild agita-
tion or nervousness (aka TRUST)
Separation anxiety anyone? I remember the first
few times leaving my toddler son with a sitter for
approximately three minutes. He showed something
substantially stronger than mild agitation or nervousness. I think snot actually came out of his tear ducts.

◇ *Say Hello –Willingness of dog to visit a person*
(aka BODHICHITTA)
What is my degree of willingness to take on the pain
of another? Can I cultivate pure loving kindness? Do
I offer my supreme good heart without holding back?

I scored significantly higher on the Which Kitchen Utensil Are You? test than the Canine Readiness Test.

Could I someday earn the right to wear the Groovy Bandana of Maximum Coolness that identifies the certified Disaster Stress Relief Dog? Maybe. And in the meantime, I have many gurus to rely upon. All of them magnificent yoga dogs. All of them natural teachers, great heroes and sublime healers. They've learned to pay no attention to the garlic fries. Can I?

Everything you know is wrong

Don't believe everything you think
Local bumper sticker

Everything you know is wrong. Remember that pithy adage? I think it was a headline for *Time* or *Newsweek* or *Mad* magazine, I'm not sure which. Like there's any difference. But I kind of liked the big bold letters screaming at me that I am completely ignorant and misinformed. Some folks get offended at this notion. Not me. I find it mockingly entertaining. But that's me. I have a certain appreciation for Sacred Irony.

The economy stinks, the war(s) rages on, the planet is in crisis and Octomom has been given her own reality show. Do I still believe that if I work really hard and save and invest, I'll be secure in my golden years? If I eat pure, organic foods and behave myself, I'll enjoy perfect health and live to a ripe old age? If I show up every day and put in a day's work for a day's wage, I'll always be employed and enjoy the fruits of my labor? Not so much. Not anymore. *Everything you know is wrong.*

Everyone is being shaken to the core these days. Our financial stability has been blown apart. Trust has been abandoned. Our identity, our very foundation, lies in ashes all around us. We lift our tired eyes and ask feebly, "What do I do now? Who am I now? Am I safe, ever? What the hell is going on here!?"

Honestly. I have many beloved friends who have been laid off from longtime careers, lost large amounts of invested monies, and seen their life's savings shrink. It's interesting to observe how we each handle the situation. Some of us are graceful and accepting in these trying times. Some of us have completely lost our minds.

As I witness the chaos being created by the unpredictability of the financial markets, I ponder: What's the source of *my* security? What gives *me* the feeling of protection? Because I have no material wealth, I've lost nothing in the economic hijinks. So I ask, What am I anchored in? What am I afraid to lose? Relationship? Reputation? Health? Publishing a column in a local newspaper?

If I identify with my stuff, or my story, then I am relying on external sources to dictate who I am and how I feel safe. And so the real question becomes, who am I *without* my stuff? Who am I *without* my story? *Without* my feelings of being heinously victimized by the cruel and dastardly Masters of Industry who created this mess and ruined my life? Meditating on these questions is a powerful practice. Who am I without my yoga practice? Without my health? Would losing all the money I have change that? Would losing my beloved Yoga Tribe change that?

Yoga says there is no security, no fixed identity to protect. We are fluid, flowing, not solid or static. Pema Chödrön writes, "As long as we believe there is something that will permanently satisfy our hunger for security, suffering is inevitable. The truth is that things are always in transition. *Nothing to hold on to* is the root of happiness." Such a beautiful and inspiring teaching. So difficult to practice as you realize your retirement savings have been squandered or stolen by trusted financial advisors. May Bernie Madoff burn in hell. And I mean that in only the most spiritual way.

The obvious and ordinary truth of change is universal. A skillful practitioner finds refuge deeply within her understanding that we are constantly changing. Nothing stays the same. And so she tries to relax into the not-knowing. She lightens up. She remembers that life is both glorious and wretched and this too shall pass. Even as she's opening her pink slip. And her home is being foreclosed. And she gains 20 pounds. As time marches on, these events could very well turn into the best thing that ever happened to her. Just think what it will look like ten years from now. Everything will be different. And once again, we'll receive the wise teaching, *Everything you know is wrong.* Sounds safe and secure to me.

For whom does Bell toll?

We don't see things as they are,
we see them as we are.

Anaïs Nin

On a cold January morning in 2007, in a corner of the Washington, DC Metro station, a young violinist took up his instrument and began to play. Just like any other street musician, he opened his violin case in hopes of tips. He played six Bach pieces for about 45 minutes and during that time, approximately 2,000 people went through the station.

Six people stopped to linger and listen for a while. About 20 gave him money but continued to walk at their normal pace. Several children stopped to listen, but in every instance, the parent pushed the child to move on. For his morning concert, the musician collected $32. After the hour was over, the young man stopped and silence took over. No one noticed. No one applauded.

Unbeknownst to the DC Metro patrons, the violinist was Joshua Bell, one of the finest musicians in the world. He played one of the most intricate pieces ever written, on a violin worth $3.5 million dollars. Two days before, Joshua Bell had sold out a theater in Boston where the seats averaged $100. (If you've ever seen the movie, *The Red Violin*, Bell is the soloist of the soundtrack. He was only 18 at the time! And if you haven't seen the movie, I highly, vigorously, strongly urge you to see it. Put it at #1 in your Netflix queue. Seriously.)

Joshua Bell playing incognito in the Metro station was organized by the *Washington Post* as part of a social experiment about perception, taste and people's priorities. The questions raised: In a commonplace environment at an inappropriate hour, do we perceive beauty? Do we stop to appreciate it? Do we recognize talent in an unexpected context?

This experiment seems cruelly obvious and sadly telling in our speedy, accomplishment-driven culture. I'm reminded of the utterly corny and trite proverb: Stop and smell the roses. Isn't it just so banal and syrupy sticky sweet wretchedly self-help barf-inducing? I prefer a more yogic translation: Cultivate the Big Awareness. Can I persistently practice moving from my small, tight, tunnel-vision mind that is so deeply involved in its story of being busy and rushing and planning and speeding towards the next Very Important Event or Idea and instead cultivate a more expansive, relaxed, open aware-ness of my moment-to-moment choices?

So, yeah, I stop to smell the roses. Literally. I've walked the streets of T-Town and been bowled over by the nasal ecstasy provided by some neighborhood gardens. Stop and hear the music. Literally. While our little town is certainly rampant with human musical

talent, how about deeply listening to the soft whoosh
of a raven's wings in flight? Or the mighty buzz of the
magnificent hummingbird? Stop and taste the honey-
suckle freshly picked from the corner fence. Stop to
honor the perseverance and poignancy of an unexpected
flower bursting through a crack in the K-Mart parking
lot asphalt. In my hurry to get to Bear Valley Springs
from town, I sometimes forget to notice how glorious
the mountains are. The same mountains that stole my
heart years ago and persuaded me to make this place
my home.

One possible conclusion reached from the DC experiment could be: If we do not have a moment to stop and
listen to one of the best musicians in the world playing
some of the finest music ever written, with one of the
most beautiful instruments, how many other things
are we missing? Makes me wonder if Joshua Bell was
fiddlin' outside the Frosty King during the afternoon
prison shift change, would I notice? Would I possibly
offer him the extra root beer float that comes when I
buy one and get one free?

So I remind myself to stop. Stop and notice. Stop and
be aware. Don't get so caught up in the doing that I
forget the being. Stop and soften the hard candy coat-
ing of my milk chocolate consciousness all while never
melting into the palm of forgetfulness. That's right. Palm
of forgetfulness.

Oh, stop. In the name of Love. Just stop. Before you
break my heart. Think it over.

Grappling with gratitude

Thank you fa lettin' me be myself
Sly and the Family Stone

In the spirit of the Season, I am pondering the quality of gratitude. And how each of us has so much to be deeply thankful for. And how the consistent and conscious practice of gratitude is innately life-affirming and joyous. And just how darn lucky we all are to be here. Praise be to all saints of all religions. I bow at your lotus feet and am eternally grateful for it all. Well, most of it all. Some of it all. The nice parts anyway. Wait. My gratitude practice feels a bit unbalanced.

I have come to realize that I excel at being thankful for all the beauty in life. The no-brainer stuff like sunshine and sex. But can I give thanks for the crappy stuff in life? It's easy to be thankful for good food, loving friends and kittens. What about the stuff that's not so gratitude-inducing? Can I find thankfulness for my aching right hip? How about the fly that has been slowly circling in my kitchen for the past two days, stalking me? Or Big Ticket items like war and injustice?

There's an intriguing Buddhist teaching that says:
*When I come downstairs in the morning, may I see
my worst enemy sitting at the breakfast table.* Crazy, I
know. Those goofy Buddhists. But the idea is that if my
enemy is waiting for me with a bowl of Frosted Mini
Fruity Coco Pebbles, then I'll have a strong opportunity
for mindfulness practice (possibly accompanied by
diabetic coma). Can I offer loving kindness to someone
I don't particularly like? Can I be grateful for someone
who pushes my buttons with fervor?

And wouldn't it be beautiful to be able to behave that
skillfully? I know that when I can somehow keep an
open heart, even in the face of something that makes me
want to run screaming from the room, I feel better. I'm a
shinier, happier, more peaceful girl.

One beneficial technique is to see my perceived enemy
as my teacher. I can contemplate how this benevolent
person has taken it upon themselves to be a sacred
irritant to my peace of mind so that I may learn patience
and compassion. How kind my Irritator is! How thankful I am for my generous teacher!

And I reflect on another good slogan: *No irritation,
no pearl.* Without the irritation of a grain of sand in the
oyster's flesh, there can be no pearl. The pearl requires
friction to make it smooth. So I can be grateful to my
ex-husband for his kind service on my behalf and hold
deep gratitude for his assistance in my spiritual evolution. Bless his heart.

I'm thinking that to truly, fully live gratitude in its
pure essence, I gotta be thankful for the cool and the
crummy, the happy and the sad, the sweet and the bitter.

(And really, what defines cool and crummy? But that's another column.) Be thankful for it *all*. And eventually let even the notion of *stuff* drop away and be just purely and fully thankful without any specific motivation whatsoever. Just grateful for the pure delight of being grateful. Period. Embodying the *quality* of gratitude.

In my travels to Cambodia, I visited the native nomadic river people. They live in cardboard shacks floating along the water and have nothing. I mean, nothing. Seriously nothing. My companions and I felt tears well up at the imaginings of their deep poverty until one of my wise friends noted that all the kids were running around happy and smiling and looked all loved up. Grateful just to be alive. Author Melodie Beattie says, "Gratitude turns problems into gifts, failures into success, the unexpected into perfect timing, and mistakes into important events." Like a magic wand of transformation!

So I welcome my enemy at the breakfast table and am grateful to run into my ex with his hot new girlfriend at K-Mart. After all, the more I practice, the stronger I become, the happier I become, the freer I become. In the spirit of the Season, I say: *Bring on the crap and let's get grateful!!*

Karma

All beings are the owners of their karma,
heirs of their karma, born of their karma,
related to their karma,
and supported by their karma.

The Buddha

Karma – this Sanskrit word has definitely found its way into the everyday American vocabulary. Everyone has heard the word and has some idea of its meaning. The concept even has its own American colloquialisms. What goes around comes around. You reap what you sow. Good karma. Bad karma. Instant karma. And my personal favorite, "Your karma ran over my dogma."

The actual translation of karma is *action*. It is the universal law of cause and effect. And just like all universal laws, karma has no opinion or judgment. It just is. Good action will produce a good result. Bad action will produce a bad result.

Karma should not be considered punishment or reward. Karma doesn't really care what the actions and their results are. Just like gravity doesn't care what stays grounded and what rises. As much as we might want to blame karma for some horrific experience we're having, sorry, friends. As an impartial law, karma itself can't be blamed for anything.

The greater the understanding we cultivate about this principle, the more we come to realize that our own actions have produced our circumstance. Karma just happens to be the facilitator. If you have done something meritorious, you experience pleasure and happiness; if wrong things, suffering. A happy or unhappy life is your own creation. Nobody else is responsible.

If you remember this, it becomes difficult to blame others for your sorry situations or, on the flip side, to feel others are responsible for your happiness. You are your own best friend as well as your own worst enemy. (Isn't that just so completely annoying??) The good news and the bad news is that the responsibility for your experience rests squarely on your own shoulders. Wouldn't it be just so much easier to blame or praise something outside yourself for your circumstances? Dang that yoga. It always comes back to self-study, self-mastery, self-observation.

I love this quote from the great yogi Paramahansa Yogananda, founder of the Self-Realization Fellowship and author of the classic *Autobiography of a Yogi*:

Every human being by his thoughts and actions becomes the molder of his own destiny. Whatever energies he himself, wisely or unwisely, has set in motion must return to him as their starting point, like a circle inexorably completing itself. An understanding of karma as the law of justice serves to free the human mind from resentment against God and man. The thoughts and actions of every human contribute to the good or ill of this world and all peoples in it.

I was once sitting with a group of yoga buddies and a Buddhist monk at the dinner table and the conversation turned to the practice of compassion. The question on the table was, "How do you find compassion for someone who has inflicted great pain on others? How do you abandon the urge for revenge?" My monk friend replied, "Karma. Just imagine what deep suffering this individual is creating for himself in the future. Human revenge is insignificant when you consider the tremendous anguish that his own actions will bring upon him." I found this to be a deeply satisfying response.

To take the same idea to a much smaller and completely trivial realm, a good friend of mine likes to use the term "parking karma" as we're circling the destination of our choice, desperately seeking a spot. We drive ever so slowly and chant "parking karma, parking karma, parking karma" until the ideal spot reveals itself. (The idiocy of this ritual does not escape us.) But somehow, we find it to be beneficial. We've both become much kinder drivers since we've come up with this whole parking karma scheme.

According to our universal law of parking karma, if we want to find the dream spot, we better practice some compassionate driving. If you want to find good parking spaces in the future, perform some random acts of traffic kindness today. If nothing else, this notion brings a more peaceful experience to the hours spent behind the wheel. And if we all drove with this idea in mind, well, can you imagine? Hummer and Prius working together peacefully for a more perfect transportation experience? The mind reels…

Karma also addresses the same idea as the Golden Rule. "Do unto others as you would have them do unto you." So beautifully simple. If you treat others with respect and kindness, then you benefit from the respect and kindness of others. If you're a cranky, mean-spirited snot, then you will benefit from the cranky snottiness of others. Cause and effect. Action and reaction. I'll take kindness over snot any day.

So, in reflecting on this notion of karma, consider your actions and what the effects of those actions will bring back to you. Remember that you are responsible for your own experience at every moment and choose wisely. And for goodness sake, keep your dogma away from my karma.

Let's talk Sanskrit

Good, good, good, good vibrations...
Brian Wilson

Sanskrit is the ancient Indian language of yoga. It can be confusing and difficult, but it's definitely worth a look. First off, it's a gazillion years old. Other than Pali, it's the oldest language on the planet. More importantly, it's a vibrational language. The sound is important, but it's the vibe that gives Sanskrit its power.

One of the most basic Sanskrit words, and one that is used abundantly in yoga, is the sacred syllable **Om** or **Aum**. Om has many translations, but in general, it can be thought of as the hum of the Universe. The underlying vibe to All That Is. It is said that the repetition of Aum with feeling and awareness can overcome all obstacles. All obstacles? And so why wouldn't I want to try this?

Most yoga classes will invite you to Om at either the beginning or end of class. As a teacher, I've always Aumed in my classes, whether they were held in a gym, a rec room or a yoga studio. It's tradition and it's a matter of respect.

Interestingly enough, I've been warned that Oming might be considered too controversial to some students in a non-yoga studio setting. Granted, the Om can be a bit confusing to the newcomer to yoga. Understanding that fear is generally born from ignorance, I will usually take a few moments to discuss this whole Aum mystery with new students. Happily, it has been my experience that folks really love the practice once they understand it.

If you've ever had the opportunity to chant an Om or two, you've certainly felt the power of its reverberation. Once the Om has been uttered, the resonance of the sound continues to bounce around inside your head and heart, lingering for a few wondrous moments. And if you've had the good fortune to Om with a group, you know that sound can stick with you and give you a big old kiss right in the heart.

Traditionally, Om is spelled Aum. And is chanted by starting with the "ah" sound then evolving into the "oo" sound and then ending with a long "mmmm" sound. Ah-ooo-mmm. These three distinct parts of the chant are symbolic. Beginning, Middle, End. Birth, Life, Death. Body, Mind, Spirit. Each Aum contains within it an entire lifespan. Chanting Om at the beginning of class quiets the mind and body. Only then can we move through the practice with the necessary awareness and attention that yoga demands. Employ Aum anytime and reap the tremendous benefit. Just sit quietly, chant Om and see what happens. Aum is musical magic.

Namaste (nah-mah-stay) is another beautiful Sanskrit word that you will undoubtedly hear in a traditional yoga class. It's a salutation as well as the name of a hand

posture. The Namaste pose involves the hands being
held in a prayer position, palm pressing into palm, in
front of the heart. The salutation of Namaste is usually
uttered at the end of class. The teacher will bow to the
students and say Namaste and then the students will
bow to the teacher and respond Namaste. This lovely
word translates to something like: *The Divine within
me honors and recognizes the Divine within you.* Wow.
Now, come on, that's pretty powerful. It radiates peace,
compassion and kindness.

These two Sanskrit words, Aum and Namaste, are
deeply embedded parts of any yoga practice. They bring
a beauty and history to the classroom. In my particular
tradition of yoga, the Iyengar tradition, we also use the
Sanskrit names for all the poses. This can sometimes
be bewildering to new students. But as time goes on,
the Sanskrit terminology becomes exotically intriguing.
Utthita Trikonasana (oo*thee*ta treeko*nah*sahnah) sounds
so much more interesting than Extended Triangle Pose.
Sirsasana (sheer*shah*sahnah) more fun than regular old
Headstand. And **Savasana** (sha*vah*sahnah) defies the
ordinariness of Corpse Pose.

But as our friend Shakespeare said, "A rose by any
other name…" The intention of yoga is the same no
matter what language is used. Non-violence, truthfulness, non-stealing, continence, non-greed, purity, contentment, effort, self-study, and devotion are the yogic
qualities to be cultivated whether they are in English,
Sanskrit, Japanese or German. Kindness is not limited to
any one language.

So, fear not, my yogi brothers and sisters. Don't let the Sanskrit scare you. Explore it. Drink it in fully and let the power of this practice wake you up. Come on. I give you an open invitation. In fact, I dare you. I double dog dare you. I double downward-facing dog dare you...

Poke me with a fork, I think I'm done

Life's challenges are not supposed to paralyze you, they're supposed to help you discover who you are.

Bernice Johnson Reagon

In his book, *Fire of Love*, Aadil Palkhivala tells a story of a great karate master who was asked to come to India to teach and give a demonstration on the finer points of karate to hundreds of students. Being a master, his physical being exuded the radiance that comes from living a life of heightened sensitivity to cleanliness, order and care.

The demonstration was held in a large, old school hall. During a break, the barefoot master requested to be taken to the bathroom. The students' eyes filled with horror as they knew the bathroom was filthy, with an inch of water on the floor strewn with human waste. The master said that it was all right. When they took him to the bathroom, he did not flinch. When he came out, he washed his feet with soap and water in a sink outside and carried on as if he had been taken to the Ritz.

As the story spread, a new sense of respect for the master awakened. His students realized that sensitivity to and awareness of cleanliness can and really must be balanced with the ability to tolerate its opposite when the necessity arises.

Now, compare and contrast that story of balance and wisdom with my own similar experience. Consider my somewhat different response to a difficult situation.

I've recently returned from the Joshua Tree Music Festival. We heard some awesome live music, to be sure, however, unbeknownst to the BF and me, Joshua Tree attracts a young indie desert rat crowd. Think Mad Max on a sheer, flat, difficult expanse of dirt about the size of two football fields. In our sweet borrowed van, we "parking lot camped." Two rows over from us was a ring of four ginormous RVs circled around what I swear was an inflatable nightclub sporting massive speakers blasting the perpetual drone of canned trance music.

As the temperature soared to over 1,000 degrees, I no longer felt my hot flashes because the external temperature had amazingly exceeded my internal temperature. This very white, sunscreen-slathered menopausal woman began to get a little uncomfortable. And bathrooms? There was only one flushing toilet within five miles, which I found to be critically important to me as a very white menopausal woman in the same parking lot camp as 500 other people.

I began to feel a tickle in the back of my brain. I recognized the stirring of discontent. I turned to my favorite tool, the breath. (After all, I've given birth to two children using only breath as my powerful ally.)

Breathe through the stifling heat and the sweat and the smell and the Porta Potty nightmare and the constant, relentless pounding of the deathly disco beat.

Breath, shmeath, I lost it. I melted down. I looked at my big, beautiful boyfriend and said with a distinct, clear voice and fully committed eyes, "I'm done." He knew what that meant.

Can you detect the subtle, almost imperceptible difference in the outcomes in these stories? Wise, balanced master vs. whiney, spoiled yogi. Skillful response vs. hysterical over-reaction. Bambi vs. Godzilla.

Yoga practice has a way of revealing how we handle struggle. When something becomes difficult, how do we hold up? At what point do we say "I'm done." When I'm practicing asana poses, and the actions of the pose become challenging, how do I respond? What does my inner voice whisper and/or scream to me? Do I listen to that voice? *Who is that voice??*

Hey, it's easy to practice when everything is comfortable. Add a bit of resistance, conflict, difficulty, and that's when the real practice begins. As I learn to find a peaceful way to stay in a challenging pose, I also learn a mindful way to stay in a challenging life situation. As I slowly add another minute to my time in headstand, I learn to add another minute to my sense of calm when faced with difficulty.

And as I sit mindfully in the harsh heat of the desert, I can recognize its beauty all around me. Even the parking lot disco.

Notes on non-attachment

*Our greatest attachment
is not to our loved ones,
or our possessions.
It's to ourselves.*

Lama Surya Das

Who doesn't love a big steaming bowl of non-attachment??

In the yogic perspective, non-attachment means not being attached to objects, ideas or beliefs. Non-attachment is to be cultivated so that we can experience a peaceful mind at all times. After all, as you may recall, the aim of yoga, according to the Yoga Sutras, is *the cessation of the fluctuations of the mind.* In other words, being able to quiet the incessant demands of our frantic minds (sometimes referred to as 'monkey mind' – I've always loved that term. It paints such a wonderfully descriptive picture of our wildly untamed minds jumping from idea to idea to try to bring satisfaction to our feral grey matter).

In cultivating this concept of non-attachment, yoga asks us to dissolve our personal desires. The Sanskrit word for non-attachment is **vairagya** (not to be confused with Viagra which is a subject for another time). Vairagya translates literally as colorless. Every desire brings its own color to the mind. When the mind is tossed by desire, there won't be peace or rest in the mind.

Truth be told, all our suffering, worry and stress comes simply from our attachment and clinging to our personal stuff; whether it's tangible objects or deeply ingrained ideas. Haven't you ever had the experience of achieving some long sought-after prize and then worrying yourself stupid that you're going to somehow lose that prize? We snag our perfect job, and then start to worry about losing it. We find the perfect mate, and then start to worry about losing our Johnny Depp to some hussy at City Slickers. The more we have, the greater the worry, stress and suffering about losing it all.

So this is where the whole non-attachment thing comes in. Non-attachment says that we can have whatever we want, but let's not allow those things to define who we are. Non-attachment says give up your expectations. Detachment can be likened to the attitude of a doctor towards her patient. She treats the patient with greatest care, skill and sense of responsibility, but does not become emotionally involved so as not to lose her faculty of reasoning and professional judgment.

When we are attached to a person, place, or thing, we will inevitably suffer. Because we expect that person, place or thing to *not change*. To always be just as we expect it to be. Just think of losing something that you hold dear. A special object, a loved one, or even your own reputation. Losing any of those items will bring tremendous distress because we are so strongly attached to them.

If you hear of someone losing their wallet, you may have a temporary thought of empathy for them, but if you lose your own wallet, you make yourself crazy. I've lost all my money, my credit cards, my driver's license, the pictures of my kids! Tears and great gnashing of teeth will ensue. Your friend's wallet doesn't mean much to you, you're not attached, but your own wallet, well, now that's a different story. Because we're deeply attached to our own stuff.

When I bring a big bowl of hummus to my friend's house for munching, can I leave my Tupperware bowl with her without demanding its return? Will I worry if I'm ever going to get that precious bowl back from her? Will I begin to build resentment towards her because I've only got three Tupperware bowls and I need them all!? How attached am I to my Tupperware? How much suffering can Tupperware really cause? (Not that I've ever had this experience, you understand. This is all hypothetical, of course.)

According to the yogic view, to achieve real peace of mind, you must be desire-less. But it is the nature of the mind to desire! The secret is to understand that without any personal or selfish motive, desire cannot bind you because pure, selfless desire has no expectation so it knows no disappointment. If you're not attached to the outcome, you will not experience suffering.

A sister friend of mine has a brilliant notion I like to refer to as the Four Step Plan to Peaceful Interaction.

The plan states: (1) Show up (2) Tell the Truth (3) Listen to what the other person is saying (4) Don't be attached to the outcome. How glorious! I love this Plan.

The next time you find yourself facing a tricky confrontation, give this Plan a shot. The first three steps are difficult, to be sure. Sometimes just showing up can be the hardest part, but step four is critical. You can do the first three, but if you skip number four, if you're attached to the outcome going in the direction of your own selfish desire, you're in for some serious misery. Trust me on this. But if you can perform all four steps with a pure, generous heart, then congratulations! You've made it to the Yogi Hall of Fame and a contented, peaceful mind is your prize.

When we cultivate a mind free from personal interest, we can live our lives sweetly and feel joyful. By renouncing our strong attachments to stuff and/or our feeling of righteous entitlement, we can possess the most important sacred property: peace.

Ringing the mindfulness bell

Therefore, ask not to know
for whom the bell tolls,
it tolls for thee.

John Donne

I have a dearly beloved friend who has the unique habit of making a clicking sound while sucking on her teeth. It's like she pulls the air into the sides of her mouth and then sucks her tongue and clicks. (Imagine the sound a rider makes as she urges her horse to giddy up.) She usually does it whenever there's silence in the room. (She's not one to enjoy silence. Silence must be filled with humming or tapping or this weird sucking sound.)

I've actually counted the number of times she's done this as we take long car trips. I'm sure she's completely unaware of her habit while I, on the other hand, am acutely aware of her habit. I'm excruciatingly aware, painfully aware, agonizingly aware. In other words, her mindless habit is a source of torturous agony for me. Annoying is almost too light a word, too forgiving.

She annoys the hell out of me. Or, more exactly, her habit annoys the hell out of me.

C'mon, now. You must know someone who has a habit that makes you into a crazy person. (Perhaps a family member or mate? And if you say no, you're a damn liar.) Some insanely insignificant thing that just sends you over the edge? And how can they be so blissfully unaware that they are dancing on your last nerve?? If only they could just shut up or stop coughing or cease their endless sniffing or clicking or scratching. Don't they see how they're disturbing you? *How can you possibly practice peace when your neighbor relentlessly continues to click her teeth?*

Where is the way out of this mental torture of the vexing habit of my dear friend? Firstly and most importantly, I have to understand that it's not my friend that is causing my unhappiness and annoyance. Blaming others is fun, to be sure, but not very wise. To find any true peace, I must shift my perception. Instead of blaming my friend for being such a blatant obstacle to my serenity, I must turn the light of awareness onto myself and observe how easily I'm pulled off center. Just some simple teeth clicking can turn me from a non-violent, compassionate yogi into an agitated, wild-eyed fiend. Really? After 13 years of practice? Well, uh, yeah.

Many spiritual communities have a ritual of ringing the "mindfulness bell." At the sound of the bell, each member of the community stops whatever they are doing and takes a few conscious breaths, bringing their awareness back to center while remembering their true Self, and then returns to whatever job they were doing with a renewed presence. This happens throughout the day so they are continually reminded to be fully aware in whatever action they're undertaking.

Imagine such a practice! So as I'm cleaning the toilet, balancing my checkbook or shoveling snow, I'm gently and continually reminded to be present with who I truly am. My true nature. My eternal Self.

I decided to tweak the idea of the mindfulness bell and in that dreaded teeth sucking sound, I hear the call of Yoga saying, "Hey! Wake up! Look at how easily you can be disturbed and pulled off center. Drop your judgments for a minute. Practice some patience. Practice some mindfulness, because damn, girl, you're an easy mark if a little teeth clicking is all it takes."

And then I get to have a good laugh at myself and get ready for the next teeth suck as a ringing of the bell. Because it will come soon enough. And again. And again. And again. Can I begin to see that wretched habit as a thoughtful assistant in my mindfulness training? As a kindly reminder to be present and accepting?

Well, sometimes, yes. And then sometimes... uh... NO. Practice. Practice. Practice.

Notes on Satya

Truth is the only safe ground to stand on.
Elizabeth Cady Stanton

Satya (saht-yah), the second **Yama** (yah-mah), translates as non-lying, truthfulness, sincerity, non-exaggeration. It implies a sincere wish to be completely open, forthcoming, and reliable. Accurate, trustworthy, factual. Unembellished. Unfiltered. The instruction is clear. Be truthful. Every code of human ethics refers in some way or another to truth telling. Plain and simple. Do not lie. We all know it. So why can that be so insanely difficult?

Have you noticed yet that lying never works? Never. Have you ever told a lie that you could really feel good about? That brought you the happiness and satisfaction that you had lied for? A lie that didn't come back to bite you in the behind at some point in time? (You're a liar if you answered yes.) As we all know, once that first lie has escaped from your mouth, then there comes a relentless landslide of other lies that must be layered onto that first lie and then suddenly, there's just so much complicated nonsense you've got to keep straight. It's exhausting.

Being honest just makes life so much simpler. But nobody said it was easy. The next time you catch yourself tempted to tell a lie, try to stop for a moment and observe your motivation. This is what yoga asks us to do. Cultivate self-awareness.

A few days ago, my daughter asked me how much I weigh because I want to go for a ride with her on her new groovy Vespa-style scooter and it has certain weight limitations. I was soooooo alarmingly tempted to lie. After a moment's awareness, I went against every fiber in my being and just blurted out my true weight. She acted appropriately appalled and we have a date to ride next weekend. Case closed. Immense amounts of drama dropped.

This is practicing my yoga. Such a breakthrough! Can enlightenment be far behind?? But the point is, if we start practicing at these shallow, simpler little levels, then when it gets to the Big Time, when the inevitable temptation to lay out a Big Whopper is staring us square between the eyes, we'll have some good experience and practice of restraint under our belts. Practice, practice, practice.

And, of course, Satya is more than just telling the truth. It's being the truth. As Shakespeare advised, "And this above all, to thine own self be true, as so it must follow as the night the day, thou canst not be false to any man," or something to that effect. In other words, be yourself. No need to go putting on airs. Or trying to be something that you're not. Honor yourself enough to be brilliantly honest in who you are. Just put it out there, from your deepest core to your shiniest smile. That's practicing yoga.

Further, in the yogic tree, non-violence comes first, then truthfulness. This is not by chance. According to yoga, kindness should always take precedence over honesty. Brutal honesty can be just that. Brutal. As every man knows, when your woman asks if her outfit makes her look fat, what is always the correct answer?? That's putting kindness before honesty. (And your own personal safety before a potentially life-threatening situation.)

So what does all this have to do with my yoga poses, my Downward-Facing Dog, Triangle Pose or Headstand? Well, can I cultivate honesty in the effort flowing into each pose? Can I bring awareness into my pose so the body moves evenly and completely? Using the body as a tool to discriminate beneficial (truthful) and non-beneficial movement, can I develop an awareness of what my body is capable of and what is inappropriate?

In conclusion, Satya is more than just speaking the truth, it's living your truth of who you are. Expressing yourself truly and honestly. The yogi is genuine in word and deed.

Satya is leading from the clear light of the heart. Being fully yourself. Cultivating an honesty practice on a daily basis. And keeping the spine extended in Dog Pose. And straightening the arms fully in Triangle. Or stretching the legs completely in Headstand. Honestly. Truthfully. Sincerely.

Yoga as religion... or not

*Sometimes the mother feeds the child
from a different plate just for variety,
but the same food still comes to the baby.
It doesn't matter which plate we eat from
as long as we eat.*

Swami Satchidananda

FAQ: Is yoga a religion?

I know that this is a point of confusion for lots of folks. And when I tell people that I'm a yoga instructor, I often get the one-eyebrow-raised-in-suspicion face as they draw back in apprehension. "Oh really? A yoga instructor, eh? So you're one of them pretzel-legged, incense-burning, tree-hugging, head-standing, godless, hippie, vegetarian, incantation-chanting freaks of nature?" To which I proudly answer, "Yes." (Please remember I am a native Texan and have actually had this conversational exchange on more than one occasion.)

When I came to glorious Tehachapi, I was warned by more than one caring individual that I might run into some "trouble." You know, being a yoga teacher and all. 'Cause that yoga stuff, that's some scary, threatening craziness that will not be tolerated in this moral, virtuous and reverent community. I could get run out of town, tarred and feathered, tied to the back of a pickup and dragged down Tehachapi Blvd for all to see.

But I knew, in my yogi heart, that the only reason people think that yoga is weird, or threatening, is because they don't know the truth about it. They're uneducated. Or maybe more precise, mis-educated. Yoga is completely moral, virtuous and reverent. And since so many people, even many who regularly practice the physical aspects of yoga, are a ball of confusion on this topic, let me clear the air.

Yoga is not a religion. Not in and of itself. Religion implies adherence to a very specific set of beliefs, usually laid down by a divine Being or a human being inspired by the Divine. And that Being is the object of devotion. Another aspect of religion can include the unhappy consequences when the system of beliefs is not followed by the practitioner. You know, the burning fires of hell and all that.

Yoga does not include any specific object of devotion. And the only consequences of not practicing yoga is a wild, untamed mind. Yoga is the science of quieting the mind. In meditation, we don't pray *to* anyone or anything, we simply try to calm the unbridled monkey mind. And then, with a balanced, controlled mind, the practitioner can use that awareness to explore their own personal, chosen deity if they like.

Yoga can be a tremendous support of any and all spiritual practice. The Yoga Sutras, Chapter 2, Verse 44 states: "Self-study leads towards the realization of God or communion with *one's desired deity*." See how that works? One's desired deity. Another translation puts it this way. "By study of spiritual books comes communion with *one's chosen deity*." It doesn't state any particular spiritual books. It doesn't have a forbidden list of undesirable literature. And then there's a third translation, "Self-study deepens communion with *one's personal deity*." Desired, personal deity. Yoga doesn't insist on any particular deity, that's up to you.

So whether your desired deity is Jesus or Gautama or Abraham or Larry, Curly or Moe, yoga can support that. The first 10 precepts presented for the study of yoga are the moral practices of non-violence, truthfulness, non-stealing, sexual restraint, non-hoarding, cleanliness, contentment, effort, self-study and study of ancient texts, and devotion of all efforts to God or *one's chosen deity*. That's all really good stuff no matter what perspective you hold. Yoga is a most inclusive, all-are-welcome, open-to-everyone kind of system. (Yo, everybody! Come on down!!)

Within the science of yoga are the tools of morality, meditation, and self-awareness. The intention of a yoga practice is to bring peace and ease to the mind. Not threatening, not scary, not intimidating. If you want to talk threatening, scary and intimidating, let's study the aspects of standing on your hands. Or doing a full backbend. Or full spinal twist. Now, that, my friends, can be some scary stuff. But not the philosophy of yoga. That's just goodness and kindness and love for your fellow humans.

But, hey, just in case you should someday see a
50-something woman covered in tar and feathers being
dragged down Tehachapi Blvd behind a pickup truck,
do give a shout out and say a prayer to the *deity of your
choice* for my quick and spontaneous enlightenment.

Mantra on my mind

Wherever you are, be there.
Unknown

Early morning. Yogashanan hits the meditation cushion.
Sitting tall, I close my eyes and place my hands on my
lap, thumbs gently touching, and begin to draw my
attention inward. I observe the effortless movement of
breath as the body drinks in the cosmic life-force known
as *prana* in yoga.

I begin to count the breaths. Inhale, one, exhale, two,
inhale, three, exhale, four... *(did I turn the alarm off?)*...
inhale, five... *(geez, traffic is really loud today)*... exhale,
six... *(there goes my achy hip)*... inhale, seven... *(can't
wait to try my new coffee... Do I have milk?... I'm so
sad I chipped my coffee cup yesterday... Chuck gave
me that cup for Mother's Day, like, twenty years ago...
I still can't believe he's dead... Wonder how I'll die...
hope there's no pain... My hip hurts... maybe I'll walk
today... I could walk to Rite-Aid for an ice cream...
who invented ice cream?... Whatever happened to Ben
and Jerry?... They sold out... greedy dairy pushers...)*
Inhale? Exhale? What? Where'd I go??

This is a typical scenario in my meditation practice. From sitting tall and mindfully watching the breath to forming an opinion on how Ben and Jerry sold out. From zero to monkey mind in 2.5 seconds. Taming the wild mind is no easy task and knowing this, I employ tools to help soothe that savage mental beast. One tool I often rely on is **mantra**.

Mantra is any word or syllable used as an object of concentration. Traditionally mantra is defined as "that which 'protects' (tra) the 'mind' (man)." (And honestly, whose mind couldn't use a little protection?) The continuous chanting of the mantra, a practice referred to as **japa**, induces a heightened state of awareness as the meditator's mind becomes mixed with the sacred sound. This recipe of sacred mantra mixed with alert mind, cooked over the flame of devotion can result in a pretty sweet cake of happiness.

Because the mental attention becomes so intimate with the mantra, the choice of sound/word should represent a beneficial or virtuous quality. **Om**, perhaps the best known traditional mantra, represents the hum of the Universe, the sound of Creation, the Divine Utterance. Using words like Peace or Love or Compassion can be very compelling. I recently discovered the mantra of Yes. Repeating Yes over and over in my mind brings a quality of spaciousness to my meditation. My heart seems to crack open a bit more and my willingness to expand my point of view is enhanced. The Yes mantra inspires an inclusive and optimistic energy. Sweet cake of happiness indeed.

Mantra use is not limited to meditation practice.

When faced with a difficulty or upset, mantra can come in very handy. As I find myself contemplating the gluttonous ecstasy of finishing the entire bag of potato chips, I can use mantra to help me close up the bag and put it away. I can om that bag of chips right back into the pantry.

Beloved spiritual teacher Eknath Easwaran, in his book *The End of Sorrow: The Gita for Daily Living*, compares the mind to the restless trunk of an elephant. In India, elephants walk in ritual processions winding through town on their way to temple. The trunk is constantly searching, always moving, and as the elephant glides through the narrow streets of the bazaar, she is tempted by countless shiny tasty things displayed in the vendor booths. If the shopkeeper doesn't watch, the wandering trunk will abscond with many precious items. But the wise elephant handler knows her habits and as the procession begins, he gives the elephant a short bamboo stick to hold. The elephant holds the bamboo firmly and walks through the streets without confiscating anyone's property. Bamboo stick as mantra.

When we repeat mantra, we give the mind a stick to hold and instead of pursuing shiny, sparkly distractions (potato chips, past regrets, future fears), it has something to hold onto. With practice, the mind is made firm, secure, and steadfast. Hmmm. Steadfast. Imagine how you'd feel after a dedicated time of silently repeating Steadfast in your mind?

Cherries Garcia be damned. I'll have the Chocolate Malted Mantra of Steadfast served on the sweet cake of Happiness. And a small bag of chips on the side. Om.

Yes, Master!

*The mind makes a wonderful servant
and a terrible master.*

Not sure

In my search for the originator of the above provoca-
tive proclamation, I found more than one answer. (PT
Barnum is said to have stated that *money* is a wonderful
servant and terrible master. But that's another story. Just
ask the clowns at Goldman Sachs.) Wonderful servant
and terrible master. I've reflected on this teaching time
and time again.

In the art and science of yoga, the aim is to quiet the
fluctuations of the mind. A happy headstand is a nice
by-product of asana practice, but the true aim of yoga is
to calm that monkey mind with its incessant chatter and
pushy ideas. But how do I make that tricky mental shift
from servant to master? Am I a slave to my thoughts
or am I the master of my thoughts? Who's in charge
anyway? I want to speak to the manager!

In Chapter 1, Verse 12 of the Yoga Sutras, Patanjali
writes, *"Practice (abhyasa) and Detachment (vairagya)*

are the means to still the movements of consciousness."
In the next line, he defines practice as *"the steadfast
effort to still the fluctuations of the mind."* He continues to sharpen the definition in the next verse, *"Long,
uninterrupted alert practice is the firm foundation of
stilling the fluctuations."* And finally he ends the section
by defining detachment as *"the consciousness of one
who is free from craving and desires."*

Just four little verses, or *threads* as they're called.
These threads are woven together to form the fabric of
our liberation. Liberation from the bossy ego-mind and
its relentless dedication to its own supremacy. Freedom
from the slavery of our conditioned thinking.

Practice and Detachment are two sides of the same
yoga coin. Just like inhale and exhale, both are essential
to experience growth. Practice brings evolution and
Detachment supports involution. Maintaining balance between the two is crucial. Can I strengthen my
efforts without strengthening desire? When I sit on my
meditation cushion, do I have an agenda? And there's
that whole *"long, uninterrupted alertness"* part of the
instruction. How long? You mean, like more than one
session once a week? And how uninterrupted? Does
texting between breaths count as an interruption?

When I made the decision to discontinue my pursuit
of the almighty Iyengar Certification, I unknowingly
shifted the balance of my practice. In disengaging
from that self-imposed goal, I was liberated. I recently
attended a teacher training intensive and was astonished
to discover all the lessons centered around preparing
for the difficult Assessment Test. A veritable No Yogi

Left Behind approach. I wondered if my newfound detachment would remain steadfast as I studied with my former colleagues. Would I feel the old, familiar urge to learn what's necessary to pass the test, forgetting that my true reason for studying was to become a more skillful teacher with improved insight and a finer understanding? Am I the master or the slave?

I found those pesky fluctuations of my mind quieting as I detached from my previously desired outcome of passing the Test. What a tremendous change in the way I showed up at the trainings! The tyrannical mind of Hey, You Need to Be Certified to Be Worthy had been vanquished. The monkeys were starting to settle down. Aaaahhhh.

Practice and Detachment are sometimes referred to as the wings of yoga. Just as a bird cannot fly with only one wing, a yogi cannot soar to self-realization without the balance of these two teachings. In my own peculiar mind, I like to think of Practice and Detachment as the two legs of yoga. We need them both as we stumble towards Enlightenment.

Sometimes one leg drags the other along. Sometimes we have to hop on one foot before the other is ready to hold some weight. Maybe we stub the toe of Self-Awareness. But being steadfast in effort and free from selfish desire, we can catch ourselves mid-stumble and bring equanimity back into our gait. Standing firmly on the balanced foundation of Practice and Detachment, we lessen the tendency to be the slave to our bossy minds and become the master of our experience.

Notes on obstacles

If you can find a path with no obstacles,
it probably doesn't lead anywhere.

Frank A. Clark

In the Yoga Sutras, Patanjali writes that there are five basic obstacles to the aim of yoga. And as I know you have all committed to memory by now, the aim of yoga is...... is...... come on, now, I've mentioned it at least six times in past columns... let's say it all together... *the cessation of the fluctuations of the Mind.*

That's right, yogis! Gold stars and tofu ice cream for everyone.

So there are these Five Basic Obstacles – in Sanskrit, **kleshas** (*klay*-shuhz). As the sutras go on, there are actually many more kleshas, but for our purposes, we're gonna stick with the basic Five. The Big Five. The Nickel-bag of Spiritual Snafus. The yogic El Cinco de Stumbling Block. And they are, in a very specific order: (1) Ignorance (2) Ego (3) Attachment to Pleasure (4) Aversion to Pain and (5) Clinging to Life.

First up is Ignorance. Note: Ignorance, not stupidity. Ignorance carries with it an air of innocence – simply uneducated, uninformed, unaware. While good old stupid carries with it an air of... well... stupidity. Dull, dense, thick, vacuous. It implies that, damn it all, you should just know better. (Ignorance is not knowing how to properly do a headstand. Stupidity is just throwing yourself, willy-nilly, into a headstand anyway without any kind of preparation or proper instruction.)

Of course, in the yogic sense, Patanjali shoots right past my clever headstand parody and heads for the juicy stuff. He refers to Ignorance as our misunderstanding of our true nature. Thinking that we are separate from the greater scheme of things. Identifying ourselves as independent from the great universal energy. And Ignorance is considered the fertile source, the breeding ground, the fountainhead from which all the other obstacles spring.

Next up is the bad boy of all bad boys, Ego. Actually, I take that back. The ego has gotten a bad rap. A healthy ego is absolutely essential for a safe and sane life. It's the inflated ego that's the troublemaker. Ego as in egotistical, self-centered, narcissistic, self-seeking, self-absorbed, self-serving, self-indulgent, self-important. Feeding that gigantic ego is an endless job. Its loud and relentless demand for attention and cooperation is unceasing. The ego wants constant petting and reassurance that it is in charge. Kind of like a bratty two-year old.

Thirdly, there's my personal favorite, Attachment to Pleasure. Why does this always have to be a problem from a spiritually revolutionary standpoint? I mean, come on. I'm doing the best I can to be kind and helpful and compassionate to all living beings. Why is my constant, vigilant race towards what feels good such an issue? (Remember the ignorance vs. stupid thing? I just crossed over into stupid.) Whatever. I get it. Desire is unquenchable. And the constant pursuit of pleasure will lead me into a rabbit hole of such epic proportions that I may never find my way out. (Addiction, anyone?)

Next comes Aversion to Pain. This, to me, is a no-brainer. Everyone wants to avoid pain, whether it be physical, mental or emotional. Unless you're some kind of sadomasochistic nut job, it's our nature to run like hell from pain. Pain, sorrow and misery trigger a chain of hate or aversion. And there's nothing like these negative states to ignite that gnawing mental chatter that is the farthest thing from (all together, now) the *cessation of the fluctuations of the Mind.*

Last, but certainly not least, is Fear of Death or Clinging to Life. As BKS Iyengar writes in his translation of the Yoga Sutras, "Love of life is sustained by life's own force. This urge for self-perpetuation is so strong that it does not spare even the wise, and is an affliction for them and the ignorant alike." Hmmm. So the wise and the ignorant are on the same slippery slope with this one.

But here's the good news. Mr. Iyengar goes on to write that as one continues the practice of yoga, "the student penetrates deep within himself. He perceives that there is no difference between life and death, that they are simply two sides of the same coin. He understands that the current of self, the life-force, active while he is alive, merges with the universe when it leaves his body at death. Through this understanding, he loses his attachment to life and conquers the fear of death." Right on. Sounds good to me.

So these Five Obstacles, the Kleshas, are given to show us how and where things can go wrong. Yoga says be mindful of these obstructions. When you're experiencing mental anguish, take a look at the Fearsome Fivesome. If I were a betting yogi, which I certainly am not because that would be against my yogic principles – okay, maybe one of those cross-grid Superbowl football pool thingies – I would wager that the anguish has somehow sprouted from one of the five kleshas.

And although the kleshas are always loitering around the alleyways of our mind, we can strive to overcome. How does one overcome them? Back to Mr. Iyengar. He writes, "If a seed becomes parched, it cannot germinate; so one must render an affliction sterile by tracing it back to its source. The father of afflictions is the mind, whose movements should be directed inward by the yogic process of involution (meditation, self-study, withdrawal of the senses)."

So, let's get busy, my yogi brothers and sisters! Slash away at those daunting obstacles with the sword of yoga. Go in. Check in. *Involute.*

With a sangha in my heart

I get by with a little help from my friends
John Lennon

Okay, so I'm a little confused. Well, not so much con-fused as mindless. Or maybe stupid. Well, stupid may be a little strong. No, actually I think stupid works fine in this instance. Stunningly stupid.

I must start this chapter of STE with a big, fat correc-tion. It would seem that my brain went into vapor lock as I was writing my last column and in my self-righteous rant concerning the history hijacking by the Texas School Board, I made some snarky comments about *Eugene McCarthy* when I really meant *Joe McCarthy*.

Presidential candidate? Un-American Activities zealot? What part of that is confusing? I was talking about Joe, but I wrote Eugene. I am grateful to Judy and Dick and tens of others who kindly brought my attention to my gaffe. You didn't laugh and point or call me a moron or anything. Well at least not where I could see you.

That thoughtful, gentle steering and guiding and correcting of another brought to mind the term **sangha**.

Sangha (*sahng*-ha) is Sanskrit for community or assembly.
Classically it refers to a community of ordained Buddhist
monks and/or nuns. These days the definition has broad-
ened to include any spiritual community or assembly
of practitioners. Surya Das defines sangha as *spiritual
friendship*. Sweet. (Not to be confused with *best friends
with benefits*, which is a slightly different situation.)

Sangha is one of the Three Jewels of Buddhism, one
of the basic tenets of Buddhist practice. *I and all sentient
beings, until we achieve enlightenment, go for refuge to
the Three Jewels – the Buddha, the Dharma (the teachings) and the Sangha.* This is a core instruction. The Three
Jewels are considered to be protection from the obstacle
of samsara, the relentless cycle of birth and death.

The sangha reminds us of what's important. They
keep us on track and wake us up. Certainly a sangha
is there for comforting when we're suffering and as
cheerleaders when we're celebrating. But an even deeper
practice is this idea of relying on sangha to keep us
honest and real and true. I had the profound experience
of witnessing two sangha brothers proclaim, "I depend
on you to tell me when I go off track. If I wander too far
from the path, be my guide. I'm relying on you." This is
powerful stuff and denotes authentic responsibility for
others. Am I my brother's keeper? You bet I am.

I have been the receiver of the sangha's wisdom
on many occasions. In my enthusiasm to create fun
weekend workshops, I used to insist on a Talent Show
for Saturday evenings and participation was manda-
tory. (Please understand my definition of talent meant
anything. I pogo-sticked. We shuffled off to Buffalo in

a tapping frenzy. It was a daring display of question-able skills.) Then my very dear friend and fellow yoga teacher gently informed me that I was the only one that really enjoyed the Talent Show. What? I'm the only one enjoying this dazzling cavalcade of entertainment? I was crushed by everyone's great relief and celebration of Yogashanan's Variety Show being cancelled.

In our devotion to the sangha, it is essential that we retain a sense of loving kindness. None of the folks who wrote me said, "Hey, dumbass, you meant Joe McCarthy, right?" They were all very benevolent with their justifications that I'd just made a typo and how silly of me and I'm just waaaaay too smart to make such an obvious mistake. (Ahem.) Sangha infers deep compassion and caring, not judging and shaming. Our spiritual friends always have our best interest at heart. Always.

So, thank you to the sangha of smart and savvy readers. In my case, clearly, it takes a village.

All hail, Catalonia!!

The greatness of a nation and its moral progress can be judged by the way its animals are treated.
Mahatma Gandhi

Have you heard the latest out of Catalonia? You know Catalonia, right? No, it's not the setting for an early Marx Brothers movie. And no, it's not the little island off the coast of California. Catalonia is a region in Spain that recently passed a bit of landmark legislation. Historically significant and culturally charged, to be sure. The Catalonian parliament voted 68–55 to ban bullfighting from their province. Ban bullfighting! In Spain? Can I get an "Olé!"?

Back in the mid-60s, I was an innocent gum-smacking, Coke-swilling, pink princess phone-loving adolescent American girl on vacation with my middle-class family in Mexico City. We rode burros to beautiful waterfalls, ate tacos while wearing ridiculous sombreros and on one unforgettable day, attended a bullfight. Why my intelligent and reasonable parents thought a bullfight would be a fun way for our family to spend an afternoon, I will never understand.

I have murky memories of scorching hot sun, drippy sweat dismantling my perfectly coiffed flip hairdo, and the significant horror of watching men in sparkly outfits drive long sharp spikes into the neck of a bull. Over and over and over again. Then, with great pomp and circumstance, the last spangled guy showed up to demonstrate his über-machismo by flapping his cape in the face of a debilitated, tortured, half-dead beast. And as the matador whacked the great animal with the last devastating blows of his sword, *el toro* finally (mercifully) died. The crowd roared. The matador prissed and preened. I puked. All over my new madras pedal pushers. My mind was blown, my heart was shattered and my flip hairdo was decidedly ruined as I stumbled from the arena, shaken to the core. Ah, the blood-soaked pageantry of it all!

Fast forward to 2010 and watch me dance around the Yoga Room when I hear of the brave citizens of Catalonia. According to www.time.com, after decades of intense anti-bullfighting activism, Catalonia has become the first of Spain's autonomous regions to officially ban the sport. In 2003, the region passed a sweeping animal-protection law that restricted towns without bullrings from building them and prohibited all children under age 14 from attending a corrida (bullfight) by placing the equivalent of an R movie rating on the event. The following year, Barcelona's municipal government declared the Catalan capital an "anti-bullfighting city."

The ban campaign was led by the animal rights lobby group Prou! (Enough!) who presented officials with the signatures of 180,000 citizens who "do not believe that bulls should be stabbed to death for entertainment."

A 2007 Gallup survey showed that almost three-quarters of Spaniards have no interest in the corrida – now it's mostly tourists (thanks, Mom and Dad). And in a dazzling display of American ingenuity, the last remaining bullring in Barcelona is being converted into a shopping mall. On opening day, all leather goods and food court mountain oysters will be half price. (I'm kidding about the half-price part, but not the shopping mall part.)

One of the basic tenets of yoga, the foundation of the practice, is non-violence. Recognizing the brutality of a bullfight is a no-brainer. The animal is *killed* (hacked, mangled, mutilated) as the goal of the sport (really, sport?). Can't bullfighters just prance around and flap their capes at one of those mechanical bulls? Or better yet, maybe they should shove sharp spikes into *each other's* necks while wearing brightly sequined bolero jackets, tight knickers and ballet slippers. I guess that would be violence, too. But at least it would be mutually compliant violence. Like Ultimate Cage Fighting. Or tennis with a Williams sister.

The citizens of Catalonia are a brave bunch. Voting to ban bullfights in Spain is like Texans voting to ban Wet T-shirt Night at the Tractor Pull. It's tradition. But thankfully, we can wake up and see that some traditions no longer serve us. Especially those that are harmful to others. So Viva Catalonia! She is the first to show the way to a kinder, gentler Spanish brand.

And may we follow in that courageous wake by examining some of our own traditions/habits/customs. Do they still serve?

Cringing for the cure

*Do not do unto others as you would
that they should do unto you.
Their tastes may not be the same.*

George Bernard Shaw

In their honorable and monumental effort to continually raise money, charitable foundations are resorting to some pretty crazy stuff. I was caught (hooked!) by both these stories recently. Am I just being too sensitive? Let the rant begin…

SERIOUSLY UNCOMFORTABLE PROMO #1: Between now and May 23, KFC and the Susan G. Komen for the Cure organization are teaming up for the newest pink fundraising adventure, Buckets for the Cure™. During this awkward campaign, 50 cents from each pink commemorative bucket will be donated by KFC, with twenty-five percent of the funds raised going directly to local Komen affiliates. The flagship store in Kentucky has been painted pink for the occasion and the Colonel Sanders mascots are wearing custom pink suits to all their gigs.

As of this writing, Buckets for the Cure™ has raised more than $3 million and is on its way to the goal of a record breaking $8 million. Eat a breast to save a breast. What a tremendous gift! And how deeply unsettling. The whole thing makes the backs of my legs feel funny.

Come to find out, KFC is owned by Yum Foods, which also owns Taco Bell, Long John Silvers, Pizza Hut, A&W. (Yum!) I must admit I have some serious doubts about their level of integrity when it comes to health-conscious products. But if I buy their nutrition-ally challenged merchandise, they'll donate to a worthy cause. Perhaps KFC could team up with the American Heart Association during Nat'l Heart Month to donate profits from their new demonic Double-Down deep fried meat-on-meatwich. Uh-oh. There go my legs again.

CRINGE WORTHY CAMPAIGN #2: Join us in supporting Soroptimist International of SCV by taking part in the Second Annual High Heel-a-thon! Grab your stilettos, pumps, or wedgies and join us as we walk 150 yards to stomp out domestic violence! (Actual ad verbiage.)

Really? Did some woman actually pitch this idea? And did a bunch of other women on that committee agree? *Hey, girls! Let's all run down Main Street in high heels and raise money for domestic violence!* (Also, the unfortunate wording of *stomp* out domestic *violence*.) This good intention just seems so silly and frivolous, too Lucy and Ethel. Maybe next year we could run in French maid's outfits! Or a pillow fight! And all in high heels. Ready to spring off the starting line? Get on your mark! Get set! Cramp!

So this is my dilemma. These campaigns have grabbed

my attention because they're so good and so awful all at the same time, raising desperately needed money, but in a deeply unnerving kind of way. Using fast food to promote cancer awareness is crazy. But there it is. And it's working and making loads of cash for the Komen folks.

Is it really educating women about the dangers of breast cancer? Can fashionable shoes inspire self-esteem for abused women? Hey! After we finish this bucket of finger lickin' goodness, let's head over to the starting line at the High Heel-a-Thon for a nice long walk in our finest stilettos. It's for a good cause! And then on to the Emergency Room for a stomach pump and foot surgery. Millions raised!

Before I get too swept away by my righteous indignation, I must ask myself the same question. How far would I be willing to go for a good cause? My dad died from complications related to alcoholism. So if I got a call from Ancient Age whiskey proposing an ad campaign called "Binging for Bob," with each bottle donating 50 cents to AA, would I do it? My first husband died from asthma complications. What if Monsanto was willing to donate 50 cents from every can of pesticide sold towards asthma awareness and research?

Just how far am I willing to step outside my integrity for a worthy cause that would benefit so many suffering people? Or maybe I'll sponsor my own event: Yogashanan's Organic Vegetarian Buffet and Birkenstock Benefit. Or I could just log onto www.komen.org or www.sigscv.org and click a button. Save my feet, my own health and the health of a chicken. And, most importantly, change the lives of those in need.

Happy/sad, life/death, moth/dog

*All differences in this world are of degree,
and not of kind,
because oneness is the secret of everything.*

Swami Vivekananda

I've recently returned from a family trip to Lundy Lake Resort in the majestic Sierras. (The term *Resort* is an extremely generous adjective for this rustic fishing camp.) On one particularly auspicious morning, I discovered a giant grey-and-white moth languishing on the wet shower floor, lying on its side, one wing heavy with water and the other wing slowly flapping as if waving a sad goodbye.

Spontaneously ignited with compassion, I retrieved a newspaper from the fish gut cleaning table (!) and scooped up the struggling moth. On finding dry ground, she began to stabilize herself. Slowly. Steadily. Then keeping legs and body still, she started to flap her wings really, really, really fast. Like *vibrating* fast. I whispered to her. She vibrated again. Then suddenly, she swooped

up to my pant leg, paused there for a moment softly flut-
tering, and then flew off into the beckoning forest. Gone.

I was euphoric! I had just spent twenty minutes
having an interpersonal, mystical, *we are one* experience
with a bug. Back at the campsite, when I regaled the
family with my profound moth story, they rolled their
eyes and smirked. *Mom is such a kook.*

Two days later I was walking with my German
Shepherd friend, Babalu, who happens to be one of the
gentlest, mildest creatures I've ever had the good fortune
to know. However, on this day, from across a stunning
field of wildflowers, I watched in horror as he skillfully
chased down a ground squirrel and snuffed it with a
fatal chomp of the jaw and powerful shake of his head.

I screamed like a girl. I recoiled at Babalu's shining
bloody teeth and long, slippery red tongue literally dripping squirrel blood. His paws glistened with crimson
splashes. Babalu was energized and fine. I was energized
and not fine. Time stood still while my heart pounded
and I breathlessly stared at my canine friend, now smiling
at me through bloody teeth. I gazed into his liquid sweet
brown eyes as I wiped down his blood-stained paws and
cried for the lost squirrel. (On hearing my harrowing
tale, my boyfriend sent me a cute video of baby moose
frolicking in a lawn sprinkler. Oddly, it helped.)

The brutality of the squirrel killing juxtaposed with
the life-affirming thrill of the moth gave me pause. My
mind had been rattled, deeply, by both situations. One
experience brought sweet, euphoric pleasure and one
brought primal, heartbreaking pain. But the real truth
is that each episode was perfectly natural, without any
emotional reaction necessary. Babalu was simply being

his perfect dog self. The Lundy Moth was clinging to life, just as any being would. As an emotional human with deluded thoughts of being Master of the Universe, I projected my own feelings onto these routine events of Nature.

So my Mother (Nature) brought me two distinct lessons which continue to have a profound impact. The bloody stump of a furry body dangling from my beloved dog's mouth *and* a resurrected moth back from death's door are equal parts of being on this little blue dot hurtling through space. Life includes both. Life insists on both. So, if I can connect with the experience of a struggling moth as it fights for dear life, can I also connect with the experience of a hunter canine, exhilarated from the kill? Be present for both? Without judgment? Isn't that really being *One with It All*? And doesn't *It All* include Even the Stuff I Don't Particularly Like?

The *Tao te Ching* teaches the duality of Nature that complements each other instead of competing with each other. Birth/death, yin/yang, pleasure/pain. All are two faces of the same coin; one cannot exist without the other. Accepting and acknowledging the differences of opposite polarities helps me understand and appreciate the Universe.

Allowing Nature to take its course without any interruption or interpretation is a tricky practice. The Tao asks, *Can you deal with the most vital matters by letting events take their course? Can you step back from your own mind and thus understand all things?*

Ah, the wily ways of Mother Nature. *Mom is such a kook.*

I don't do that

My life has been one great big joke,
A dance that's walked,
A song that's spoke,
I laugh so hard I almost choke,
When I think about myself.

Maya Angelou

As a highly intelligent, deeply sensitive human, I have a good sense of who I am. I know what I do and what I don't do. I know I'm a vegetarian Buddhist yogi; organic and local; politically conscious and TV-free; riveting conversationalist; stunning beauty. It's a nice, neat little package of Yogashanan. My life's practice is about having self-awareness and I think I've got it dialed in. I've been working this whole consciousness thing for decades now. I know who I am.

On visiting my beloved and nutritionally delinquent mother, this vegetarian Buddhist yogi watches mindless television, swills Diet Coke and downs scary little snack packages of weird, unholy orange crackers and pretend peanut butter. All activities that I absolutely do not do.

I have a crystal clear understanding of who I am and what I do. And these are things I do not do. Until, of course, I discover myself doing them.

My friend Constance does not eat biscotti or drink wine. She informed me of this one evening as we were eating biscotti and drinking wine. I've often had yoga students tell me they can't balance on one leg as they do a steady Vrksasana (tree pose) which requires balancing on one leg.

Why do we do this? Ever notice that urge to put yourself in a category? Define yourself? We seem to enjoy strong ideas of who we are and what we do, whether there's any validity to those ideas or not. And the more we feed any particular attribute, the more solid it begins to feel and the boundaries of our self-imposed Box start to harden. We create a fixed notion of *me*. We write the Almighty List of Things I Do and Things I Don't Do. Our personal official manual of likes/dislikes, fair/unfair, beneficial/detrimental, paper/plastic.

Unfortunately, our idea of who we are can become rigid. So rigid that we cannot imagine another choice. Change is not an option. And ultimately, the whole mess hardens into "this is the way I am." Fixed and unyielding. No possibility for change or growth. One big solid slab of death, lurking over our shoulder, convincing us to protect the Box at any cost.

It has been my experience that something usually happens to challenge the Box. That's when the real fun begins. The challenge could come from an external source: a beloved grandson asks a technically challenged grandma to play a video game; a dancing wife requests the non-dancing husband out on the floor. Or it could be an inside job as you suddenly find yourself exhibiting a behavior that you know is definitely on the Things I Don't Do list. (Like sucking down your third Diet Coke while watching back-to-back episodes of *Law & Order*.) The boundaries are blurring and the Box has just had a hole blown through it.

Pema Chödrön, Buddhist nun and renowned teacher, refers to the idea of *flexible identity*.

With flexible identity, we throw away the Almighty List. The rock solid boundaries of the Box fade and soften. With flexible identity, we recognize that nothing remains the same, including our idea of who we are. When I'm not tied to any rigid construct of who I am, I am liberated. Flexible identity frees me up to examine things from a neutral, balanced perspective. I don't feel the urge to instantly react from any specific *(my)* point of view. Now there's room for growth and conversation. There's breathing space for evolution and understanding. I do not refer to the same Rulebook today that I was using back at Texas Tech University or as a young mother or as a newly divorced forty-something floozy. (Besides, I think I burned those Rulebooks. Or sold them on eBay.)

I am acutely aware that even with the teaching of flexible identity, I continue to make Almighty Lists. But now those Lists aren't written in stone. And when I remember that the boundaries of the Box are constantly in flux, I can relax a bit. The pressure to maintain a solid personality is relieved by the willingness to embrace impermanence. I am willing. I am so willing. After all, it's one of the Things I Do.

Local Color

*These essays all relate
to local Tehachapi issues...*

Bodhisattva, won't you take me by the hand?

My religion is very simple.
My religion is kindness.
HH The Dalai Lama

Bodhisattva (Sanskrit) bow-dee-*saht*-vuh – a being whose actions promote unity or harmony; one who chooses to postpone their own enlightenment in order to help all beings; an enlightened person or being; specifically, one who foregoes personal nirvana in order to help others achieve enlightenment. They embody unconditional love, acceptance, mercy and forgiveness and are often appealed to in times of distress for protection, comfort and healing.

Got the bodhisattva picture? These folks are here to help. They care, like, really, really care. Their devotion is unrelentingly kind. If you're not ready for enlightenment quite yet, then they'll stick around and help until you are. I, on the other hand, find it difficult to postpone my own trip to Walgreens if my friend isn't ready. But I've

received a new lesson in kindness. Oh, the deep, deep
kindness.

A real, present-day bodhisattva in Bakersfield took
me by the hand last week. *Bakersfield bodhisattva* seems
an unlikely phrase, but there it is.

The tale begins as I am late picking up my dear friend
at the Bako airport. I'm not familiar with Bako and
know only one way to get to the airport. *Take Merle
Haggard off the 99.* (Just being able to say or write that
is awesome. Another unlikely phrase, but there it is.)

As it turns out, I cannot take Merle off the 99
because it's closed for construction. And the next exit
off the 99 is nowhere in sight. I found myself suddenly
trapped on a long stretch of highway with the fuel
warning light now blinking, no idea where I am or
where I'm going, and an exhausted friend waiting for
me at the airport, wherever the heck that is. I started to
slightly panic. I could feel my lips begin to pucker and
my forehead contract. After miles of mild gut wrench-
ing, I spied an exit up ahead. At the exit was a gas
station. Hallelujah children.

The gas station harbored a beautiful dark-eyed
Hispanic woman, early 40s, cashier. I asked directions
and after a few difficult exchanges, and some vague
assistance from her completely uninterested son, I
reluctantly got back into the car and started down the
desolate looking road, anxious and unsure if I was on
the right track.

Succumbing to the only remaining shred of common sense I had, I turned around and went back to the
station. I skulked in, smiling humbly at the beautiful

woman. "Forgive me. I know you must think I'm a complete idiot but I'm still not sure where to go. Would you come outside and point for me?"

And the *bodhisattva* smiled her warm, gracious smile and *took me by the hand* and pointed me in the right direction. She looked right into my eyes and said with steadfast assurance, "You're going to be just fine. Don't worry. You're going to be alright." And I melted into her eyes. I felt completely lifted up. I floated to my car and drove off into the sunset. (My cosmic boost took a hit as I passed a feedlot with about 600 cows packed into corrals. But that's another story.)

I thought to myself, what if everyone could have this tender woman look deeply into their eyes and say, "You're going to be just fine. You're going to be alright," and then fully feel that to be true – well, wouldn't the planet be a different place? I went from anxious nutjob to serene spirit with one considerate gesture. This complete stranger gave me a comfort that I will never forget. In times of trouble, I will recall that face and her kind, compassionate eyes.

The Bodhisattva of Bakersfield. Or to be more precise, about 25 miles outside of Bakersfield. Whatever. She inspires me to pay it forward. Be the bodhisattva. No matter who shows up at my gas station. No matter how stupid they seem. Because sometimes that's all we need – just one person to acknowledge us and recognize our discomfort and unease. Just one person with a few kind words can completely shift our state of mind.

I vow to awaken my inner bodhisattva. Perhaps there's an opening at the local Chevron.

City temporarily saved from evil labyrinth scheme

Yogashanan is on retreat this week, meditating and practicing for world peace. Her column has been written by her shadow self, Snarkyshanan.

Citizens of Tehachapi! Surely we all are sleeping a little easier these days with the secure knowledge that no crazy labyrinth will be built in City (Marx) Park. At least not this year. Perhaps never before in our 100-year history has our sweet little mountain town been so deeply threatened. Thank God (and you know which God I mean) that the Tehachapi Valley Recreation and Parks District and Other Various Officials have saved us from the hideous consequences of a labyrinth in our cozy hamlet. At least for the time being.

Hey, I've read the papers. I know the scoop. As suggested by one concerned citizen, I googled "labyrinth occult." As explained by one of the website experts, "As we walk the labyrinth we are...entering into a covenant agreement with the demonic being initiated just by using the labyrinth...." Wow. Really? Would that be the mythical Minotaur I've heard so much about? Isn't he like half-man/half-bull or something? (And really, is that such a bad thing?)

Well, I've got news for you. I'm not entering into any damn covenant agreement with a demonic being in my own City Park. Sorry, but like so many other concerned citizens, I'm just not comfortable with that. (By the way, I also googled "health food occult" and "boy scouts occult." Now, there's some fascinating reading.)

Why would we want to invite such sketchy behavior into the heart o' town, Marx Park? I want to freely fly my frisbee without any irksome "public art" getting in the way. Think about it. The implications are mind boggling. Imagine people of all ages quietly and mindfully walking on a flat stone path laid into the ground, treading the circular route to the center and back again. Relaxed and reflective. Calm and quiet. Diabolical. Fiendish. Appalling.

I'm also afraid these local Labyrinth-loving kooks are gaining momentum within our community. Once they become joined with the powers of darkness and destruction, there's no telling what they might do. Minotaur and unicorns stampeding down Green Street! Tarot readings over bubbling cauldrons at the Public Library! Ouija boards at City Hall! *Where will it all end?*

Don't be fooled, my fellow T-Towners! This maintenance-free public display of ancient artwork is not what we want for Tehachapi. Never mind that these relentless Labyrinth Project geeks are willing to raise all the money themselves, *with no assistance whatsoever from any government organization.* Never mind that all the design and construction labor has been *donated* by the Masonic Lodge, who have a special spot in their collective hearts for Marx Park due to Mr. Marx being the Masonic President and all. Never mind that the volunteer LP committee has gathered over 200 signatures *in support* of the park location. All these meaningless details wither in the face of the certain depravity that the sinister labyrinth would inspire. Be gone, Mr. Minotaur! You are not welcome here!

Okay, I'm going to stop right there. Snarkyshanan has had her chance to spew and now Yogashanan must provide some balance. As a proud member of the Labyrinth Project Committee, I was sadly disappointed in the recent turn of events concerning the labyrinth location. My disappointment is rooted in my deep attachment to the City Park site. (Note to self: disappointment is always born from attachment.)

And as luck would have it, my disappointment transformed into sarcasm and snarky-ness. Not very yogic, I think, but, hey, that's why they call it a practice. But I also feel that it's a yogi's responsibility to speak out against ignorance and misinformation. To educate and illuminate. And, in this particular case, to mock and satirize. (Snarkyshanan is still working on appropriate vs. inappropriate. It's a battle.)

So I listen as Yogashanan whispers lovingly to Snarkyshanan: just relax and practice patience and acceptance. *Again.* And throw in some tolerance while you're at it. Stay focused on bringing this beautiful tool for cultivating peace into the community you so dearly love. It'll happen. One breath at a time.

That Yogashanan can be really annoying. I wonder if the Minotaur's eaten today.

Pizza Man

Work is love made visible.
Kahlil Gibran

You know that old saying about how one person can
change the world? Isn't there an old saying like that?
Well, there should be. One person with fierce willpower,
stamina and passion can really shake things up. I know
a person like that. Well, I don't actually know him, but
I know who he is. He has shaken up things quite a bit,
without uttering a sound. He is a shining beacon of
one-pointed concentration, a superb example of **tapas**,
the Sanskrit word for fiery effort and zeal. This man
has been a significant teacher for me and for countless
others. I speak, of course, of the Little Caesar's Pizza
Man at the corner of Tucker and 202.

You've seen him. He is a T-Town icon and a personal
hero of mine. I don't know his name and I like the not-
knowing. I enjoy the mystery. I can make up my own
little story of who he is and why he's so deeply committed to his livelihood there on the corner. Whenever
I drive by his post, he is in deep concentration as he

jiggles and dances his sign. He is completely present moment as he shifts his body with razor-sharp precision. In the coldest of winters, I've seen him dance the board. In the hottest of summers, I've seen him dance the board. He is Zen-like in his approach to his craft and I admire him greatly.

He is seasonally joined across the corner by Uncle Sam, the Statue of Liberty, winged angels, Santa, Prop 8 warriors and various assorted political nutbag characters (myself included). Their solitary goal in life is to get you to honk your horn. They are willing to do almost anything to win your honk of approval.

Bless their hearts, these jumping crazy kids have no real corner-working skills. They're young and rash. A friend once remarked how the young kids across the corner are just like the Pizza Man. I almost spit out my chai to immediately correct my misled companion. The kids have no flair or sophistication in their technique! Their movements, frequently fueled by an iPod, are feral and undisciplined. Their enthusiastic zeal is no match for the focused, well-honed and concentrated techniques of PM.

Pizza Man is an artist. He is completely organic, no electronics needed. He doesn't give a damn if you honk or not. His quick-tempoed bouncing knees and tight little jiggling arms are synched to perfection. The rhythmic swinging and tilting of his pizza placard from side to side is determined, almost frenetic. He never stops moving. He is relentless. He is hypnotic. He clearly takes tremendous pride in his work. He rocks my world.

I see the Pizza Man as a great yogi. He is fully present and completely involved with a laser-like focus on the job at hand. He moves as if in a meditation, fully aware and awake. Although his face suggests a long and eventful life, his quick and solid body movements do not reflect his age. He doesn't really smile much, he is too intent for that. This is serious business and he is a dedicated practitioner. Or it could just be that he's weary of the goony grinning woman who drives by and waves occasionally. As if he could wave back. His hands are busy with his work. He cannot be distracted from his purpose. He is in his dharma.

I wonder what the Pizza Man thinks of us. After an afternoon of bouncing and jiggling and paying rapt attention, does he go home and regale his family with stories of what the lunatics at Tucker and 202 did today? Do his legs and arms ache? Does his wife massage them lovingly in deep appreciation of what he gives his community? Yeah. I like that ending. I'll keep it. Hey, it's my story about the guy and I can make it any way I like.

Thank you, Pizza Man. Your powerful teachings do not go unnoticed.

How sweet it is

(from high atop Yogashanan's soapbox)

I'd like to buy the world a home
and furnish it with love
Grow apple trees and honey bees
and snow-white turtle doves
I'd like to teach the world to sing
in perfect harmony
I'd like to buy the world a Coke
and keep it company

Remember that heartwarming ad from 1970? With beautiful people from all over the planet standing on a verdant hill, holding their magical Cokes and wishing the world peace, love and carbonated sugar? Well, my friend, watch out. The times, they are a-changin'.

Fast forward to 2010. We are fat. Soda consumption is through the roof right along with diabetes, obesity and heart disease. The healthcare reform movement rages on as I catch a new TV ad depicting a suburban mom unloading her groceries with the help of her two teenagers. She looks troubled as she emotes into the camera, "In this

difficult economy, Americans are counting pennies more
than ever. A tax on simple pleasures like juice drinks and
soda is the last thing Americans need right now." The teens
look depressed over the loss of their sugary delights. It's a
gloomy, miserable day in suburbia. I laughed out loud.

Simple pleasures? The ad is in response to rumblings
from the feds and the state that a soda/fruit juice tax is
coming. In a *Men's Health* interview, President Obama
comments that a tax on soft drinks and other sugar-
laden products "is an idea that we should be exploring,"
adding that there is "no doubt that our kids drink way
too much soda."

Whoa, there, Mr. President. Too much soda? Is this
another of your socialist ideas to manipulate us into a
goose-stepping nation of conscious eaters?

A report published online by the *New England Journal
of Medicine* amplified calls for a tax on sugar-sweetened
beverages, stating that such a measure would reduce rates
of diet-related diseases and shrink healthcare costs. Then
there's the Americans Against Food Taxes Coalition who
sponsored the TV ads. Coalition members include health-
conscious businesses like 7-11, Burger King, Chemical
Industry Council, Chik-fil-a, International Dairy Queen,
Jack in the Box, National Chain of Theatre Owners,
Ron's Towing, Inc. (?), and my personal favorite,
Bowling Centers of Wisconsin. (That's the last thing this
country needs: a mob of angry soda jones-ing bowlers.)

So sugar is the new tobacco. Pepsi is the new
Marlboro and Sunny D is the new Jack Daniels. Time
for a new sin tax! (I love the whole "sin tax" moniker.
It sounds so dark and deeply wicked!) Since we can't

seem to control our decadent urges, the only way to correct ourselves is through the pocketbook. The tax on cigarettes is so severe that the hacking New Yorker now pays almost $10 for a pack of smokes.

Some say education is the answer. Is there really any confusion about Nehi as a nutritious beverage choice? And still we consume 800 billion gallons of soda. Okay, I made that number up, but you know we drink that crap like crazy. And it's costing us big-time.

But when we start to single out unhealthy foods for taxation, does that pave the way down the proverbial slippery slope? Where will it end? How about restricting the number of fast food restaurants in any given neighborhood? (Already happening.) Can we legislate ourselves into healthier bodies? Is that what it takes to slap us into awareness? Geez.

And if we're going to talk *sin* taxes, I'd like to make a proposal. Since sin is defined as "a deliberate transgression of a religious or moral law," how about taxing liars? Or bullies? If we can tax our way into a physically fit nation, could we tax our way into a kinder nation? If it's going to cost me money to be a snot to someone, would I reconsider my behavior? If I got a tax cut for being loving and forgiving, would I practice a little more?

I hear the soda tax bill being proposed for California will be numbered Proposition 8. Yep. Prop 8. Think I'll mosey on down to the Tucker/Valley intersection and enjoy a supersize sparkling water with my gay friends. Move over, Pizza Man.

This column was written in response to a brilliant practical joke played on a local restaurant. It's the only column I've ever written that was rejected by the editorial staff. I was told it was a bit insensitive to the restaurant owner. So I did a sanitized version for print. Ultimately, the whole incident became a great story point for the restaurant and the Hanging Chef was the star of the Christmas Parade. Go figure.

Maria, yogini of Austria

When the dog bites, when the bee stings,
when I'm feeling sad, I simply remember
my favorite things and then I don't feel so bad!
Maria, *Sound of Music*
(before the Nazis show up)

I don't have a dog bite, or a bee sting (although the BF did get attacked by a vicious and savage wasp), but I did catch some sadness recently and rather than wallow in self-pity (which can be extremely satisfying sometimes but not this time), I reflected on almost-Sister Maria's sage advice. As promised, the mere thought of my favorite things in T-Town filled my heart with happiness! Having a bad day, buddy? Need a rocket ride out of the doldrums, friend? Contemplate some of my favorite things about Tehachapi:

The Rancmotel sign. Who hasn't driven past this quaint little establishment and wondered, what's with that name? Wouldn't it make more sense if it were Ranchotel? That seems logical. Even kind of clever, you know, combining Ranch and Hotel to make Ranchotel. But Rancmotel? It doesn't make sense. It's like they ordered that big-ass sign from the Neon Hotel Sign-Making Factory without giving a whole lot of thought to the spelling. And I've always wondered, didn't someone at the Sign Factory think twice? Or consider making a phone call to the motel/hotel to double check the spelling before bending all that neon tubing? I take all my houseguests by the Rancmotel. It's a T-Town jewel.

Speaking of jewels, another favorite beams from the small market on Valley Blvd that advertises *Jewelry/ Meat Market.* An innovative combo to be sure. I can't

say that I've ever seen those two commodities paired. At
least not deliberately. And talk about convenience! Let's
see, I'll take a pound of pork chops, a small rump roast,
some chicken livers, oh, and that ruby-and-sapphire-
encrusted pendant. One-stop shopping at its finest. My
inner smile glows brighter at the mere thought of it.

Any T-Town parade. I'll never forget my first
Tehachapi parade experience. It was 4th of July and
hotter than blazes, but shivers of joy ran up my spine
at the dazzling display of fire engines, dump trucks,
marching bands, go-carting Shriners and dancing-school
darlings. From that first parade, I've dreamt of the Yoga
Tribe participating in this glorious festivity. And as of
this writing, we're planning our entry for the Mountain
Festival parade. I can hardly contain myself.

And my new all-time favorite thing about Tehachapi
that will always bring a smile to my face: *the theft and
ultimate hanging of Jake's Chef.*

How completely brilliant and silly and clever and
entertaining and harmless. These pranksters are freakin'
geniuses. To have stolen Chef in the first place took
great planning and skill. After all, he was bolted into the
cement in front of the restaurant. But the real beauty
part, the most astonishingly admirable part, the genu-
inely yogic part is that the tricksters waited *an entire
year* before completing their mission.

Consider the Job-like patience of waiting 12 long
months before the final taste of gratification! The sweet
agony of knowing this mischievous secret! What an
inspiring demonstration of patience for us all. And then,
these stealth-like ninjas of naughtiness suspend Chef
from the water tower under cover of darkness, using
some genius pulley contraption to heave him up there
like a portly piñata. How could they possibly sleep
that night in breathless anticipation of the morning's
revelation?

Ah, such delicious monkey business. I bow deeply to
you, O Great Hijinks Masterminds. Your creativity, skill
and amazing patience have found you a home at #1 on
my favorite things about T-Town list.

So, in keeping with the ever-perky Maria's sugges-
tion, should I suffer a dog bite or bee sting or any other
animal attack for that matter, I'll think of Chef dangling
from the Water Tower. Or Rancmotel. Or Jewelry/Meat
Market. Or Julie Andrews knee-deep in kitten whiskers.
And giggle myself back home.

Here's the cleaned-up version. Not nearly as fun.

Maria, yogini of Austria

When the dog bites, when the bee stings,
when I'm feeling sad, I simply remember
my favorite things and then I don't feel so bad!
Maria, *Sound of Music*
(before the Nazis show up)

No dog bite or bee sting here (although the BF did get attacked by a vicious and savage wasp the other day), but I did catch some sadness recently and rather than wallow in self-pity (which can be extremely satisfying sometimes but not this time), I reflected on Maria's sage advice. Having a crummy day, buddy? Need a rocket ride out of the doldrums, friend? Contemplate some of my favorite things about Tehachapi...

(DISCLAIMER: *Everyone* recognizes the deep significance of our amazing city murals, downtown charm, the Loop [both railroad and publication], stunning organic farms, and the renowned windmills. However, I feel there are several overlooked gems in our midst. And in all fairness, they should get a little look-see.) Consider:

179

The Rancmotel sign. Who hasn't driven past this quaint little establishment and wondered, what's with that name? Wouldn't it make more sense if it were Ranchotel? That seems logical. Even kind of clever, you know, combining Ranch and Hotel to make Ranchotel. But Rancmotel? It doesn't make sense. It's like they ordered that big-ass sign from the Neon Hotel Sign-Making Factory without giving much thought to the spelling. And I've often wondered, didn't someone at the Sign Factory think twice? Or consider making a phone call to the motel/hotel to double check the spelling before bending all that neon tubing? I take all my out-of-town visitors by the Rancmotel. It's a T-Town jewel.

Speaking of jewels, another favorite shines from the small store that advertises *Jewelry/Meat Market*. An innovative combo to be sure. I can't say that I've ever seen those two commodities paired. At least not deliberately. And talk about convenience! Let's see, I'll take a pound of pork chops, a small rump roast, some chicken livers, oh, and that ruby-and-sapphire-encrusted pendant. One-stop shopping at its finest. My inner smile glows brighter at the mere thought of it.

Another sign of distinction (pun intended) is at the medical office that promotes *Fracture Clinic, Upper and Lower Extremities, Wednesdays 11am–3pm*. What? No side extremities? What if I fracture something more mid-body, like, say, my pelvis? What if I fracture my pelvis on a Thursday afternoon? My longtime Tehachapi friends tell me that office used to be a Sizzler back in the day. Just another justification for my deep admiration. I'm feeling better already.

The Hitching Post Theatre. Just because it's called Hitching Post. I am from Texas, remember.

Any T-Town parade. My first Tehachapi parade experience was 4th of July, 2006. It was hotter than blazes but shivers of joy ran up my spine at the dazzling display of fire engines, dump trucks, marching bands and dancing-school darlings. From that first parade, I've dreamt of the Yoga Tribe participating in this glorious tradition. We'll be debuting at Mountain Festival. I can hardly contain myself.

HONORABLE MENTION: A Mojave minimart advertises *Ice and Ammo.* Can you have one without the other? It's always a good idea to ice down the beer before firing off your newest barrage of bullets. Love and Marriage. Bread and Butter. Ice and Ammo. It's a natural.

HONORABLE MENTION #2: The recent disappearance and stunning reappearance of a local restaurant's mascot. 'Nuff said.

So how does this jive with yoga? Yoga is ultimately about training the mind. Cultivating awareness. As the Great Ones have said, "The mind makes a wonderful slave and a terrible master." I need not be a slave to my thinking. I can practice consciously shifting my mental state to ease my suffering.

So when I find myself staring down the rabbit hole, I can consciously direct my mind towards a more beneficial state. Should I suffer a dog bite or bee sting or any other animal attack for that matter, I'll think of the Rancmotel. Or Jewelry/Meat Market. Or fez-happy Shriners careening their tiny go-carts on parade day. Or even Julie Andrews knee-deep in kitten whiskers. And giggle myself back home.

Quoth the raven,
"Where's my egg?"

Choose only one master. Nature.
Rembrandt

I have two amazing new gurus. They do not speak my
language and yet I hear their teachings every morning.
The school is way out in the country, our classroom is
the fencepost, and the lesson revolves around whole raw
eggs. But first, a little back story.

I have a beloved friend, let's call her Sue, who has
been ill recently. Because of the severity of her illness, I
decided to move into her house and force my loving care
onto her whether she liked it or not. Sue lives in one of
the most charming homes I've ever seen. A lifelong artist
and nature lover, her home reflects that sensitivity. She
has created a magical paradise for the local bird popula-
tion as bird houses and bird baths dot the landscape
of her Eden. When I asked her what I could do to help
her healing, her first request was, "Would you fill the

birdfeeders and replenish the birdbath?" No thought for herself, just her winged buds. A true yogi.

I have never been much of a bird enthusiast. My mom had parakeets during my formative years and they were always kind of nervous and panicky. When she would occasionally release them from their caged hell for an afternoon's outing, they would fly recklessly around the house, disoriented and wound up. They were just so tiny and neurotic and fragile. They freaked me out.

That being said, I've recently become a bird watcher. Not in the sense of identifying the species, that's way too technical and would actually require some knowledge. I'm talking about the pure delight of simply watching these fascinating beings be themselves. Observing them in their own environment has given me a new perception of these creatures, as opposed to the freakish flighty fear of Pepe the Parakeet wildly careening around the living room in search of any exit from his torturous existence in my family's home. Bless his teeny-tiny itsy-bitsy wildly beating heart.

And just as my perception of birds as a species has evolved, so has my perception of the much-maligned bird, the raven. My previous judgment about ravens came from the usual highly credible sources: movies and cartoons. And Edgar Allen Poe. And who could possibly forget the shocking and shamefully racist black birds from Disney's Dumbo. And of course the inimitable Heckle and Jeckle.

Well, Sue has created an incredible practice with two magnificent ravens. (And as her imposed nurse, I have now taken over this task.) Each morning, I place two

raw chicken eggs onto fence posts along her driveway
and wait for the magic to start. Spreading his great
wings, the first one sweeps down onto the fence and
hops towards his prize. I watch as he opens his huge,
heavy, sharp beak and tenderly, gently, delicately picks
up the whole raw egg. Moments later, the partner
appears. Just as her friend before her, she gingerly takes
the egg into her beak and flies away. I am completely
stunned, delighted and impressed. How sensitive! How
tender! How incredibly freakin' beautiful!

Each day I get to perform this task, I am equally
thrilled. Heading for the fencepost, I make the clicking
sound that Sue has taught me to call the ravens. I search
the sky for their black bodies and sure enough, as soon
as the eggs are in place, the ravens gracefully glide
down. I feel connected to the lives of the two lovers.
These two big birds with their sweet gentleness make

my heart smile. The crazy thrill of *simply giving* to these birds is undeniable. Can I take that undeniable thrill and apply it to all creatures? Even the human ones? Am I as willing to redefine my judgments of other beings as I am these birds?

Extra Credit Note: Long ago, when my teachers had newly learned their egg behavior and were clearly delighted at the kindness of their human friend, they expressed their appreciation. The next morning, when Sue went out to place the eggs, she found a small stone on the fence post. A "thank you" from the ravens.

Not even Heckle and Jeckle could top that.

Overstimulated in T-Town

Humanity is acquiring all the right technology
for all the wrong reasons.

R. Buckminster Fuller

It's the final moments of yoga class and everyone is moving towards a state of deep relaxation as I softly sound the gong. In a moment of unfortunate timing, my neighbor begins to play hip-hop music at a good blast. Because of my deep desire for the students to have a peaceful experience, I find it difficult to keep my mind quiet and focused. As I attempt to guide my students through a serene experience, my own mind is on fire. (Hooked.)

I am traveling to visit my precious family. When I stop for gas, a persistent video screen installed on the pump issues important bulletins on traffic jams and Suri Cruise's latest fashion accessory.

I stop at the grocery store and am slimed with yet another uninvited video screen at the check-out line broadcasting meat-carving techniques and the newest *Twilight* vampire hottie. Argh. (Hooked.)

I am riding my bike through Historic Downtown
Tehachapi during the spectacular seasonal weather.
I delight in my small-town existence, feeling that all is
well and Life is good. But, wait, there's a disturbance
in the Force. My sweet ride through town has been
thwarted by a sense of unease. Hey, where's that music
coming from? The bushes? A park bench? OMG, there's
hidden speakers in the trees. It's creepy and weird and
uncomfortable and just a bit too Stepford. (Hooked.)

Most tragic of all, my beloved Frosty King installed a
TV at the front counter. It continually blares soap operas
and I am horrified. Every waiting room of every business
that requires a waiting room houses the omnipresent
television. Always on. Always talking. Always numbing.
(Hooked again.)

Hook (or *shenpa* in Tibetan) is the term used by
Buddhist nun Pema Chödrön to refer to something
that makes us contract. Something that pulls us out of
present-moment awareness. My latest hook is this whole
media intrusion phenomenon. Because I have no access
to the *off* button, I feel oppressed by the imposed stimuli
as I pump gas, buy groceries, enjoy a meal or simply
walk down the street. And I deeply wonder, *why do we
need to fill the silence?*

In Martin Scorsese's movie *Kundun*, which chronicles the early life of the Dalai Lama, there's a scene
depicting Tibet just after the Chinese invasion. As
loudspeakers in the villages relentlessly broadcast Mao's
propaganda, the teenaged Dalai Lama sadly observes,
"They've taken away our silence." I hear ya, Your
Holiness. I get it.

I decide that I don't like this tightening in my solar plexus every time I get an unexpected hit of inflicted electronics. So now what? The technology is certainly not going away. How do I *un*hook? One teaching is *Don't get caught in the content: observe the underlying quality – the clinging, the desire, the attachment.* So the content of my hook is the uninvited media overload. And the underlying quality is the clinging to my strong personal view of how things should be. My clinging to that view has resulted in a disturbed, irritated mind which has now transformed the usually charming Yogashanan into Miss Put-Upon Victim of Electronic Imperialism, criticizing and complaining about the intrusion, the imposition, the insult of all this damn technology.

Instead of getting constricted in my heart and mind, can I relax and expand into my discomfort? Get present and tune into my breath until the feeling passes as I know it eventually will? As Kenny G and XM radio serenade T-Town from the hinterlands of the trees, can I mindfully soften my tightening jaw without trying to escape or avoid the ickiness? And most importantly, can I do it with compassion and loving kindness for myself and my irritation? And then repeat this new softer, gentler response a thousand gazillion times until it becomes habit. Hook, relax, breathe, repeat. Hook, relax, breathe, repeat. And repeat. And repeat. And repeat.

(P.S. I whined about the TV to the Frosty King staff. I told them I would no longer be enjoying my #13 Veggie Burger Combo *inside* their fine establishment. Shockingly, they didn't seem to care. They knew they'd see me at the drive-thru. Frosty fries = hook. Big, big hook.)

Millpond samadhi

You can go to heaven if you want.
I'd rather stay in Bermuda.
Mark Twain

The eighth and final limb of yoga is **Samadhi**. Samadhi can be defined as "absorption into the Divine." It's Heaven, Nirvana, Buddha Nature, Happy Hunting Ground, etc. It's the end of the line. The culmination of a dedicated yoga practice. The state of cosmic consciousness. The Happy Place.

We get glimpses of this state every now and then, perhaps in nature or meditation/prayer. Or sometimes just gazing into the eyes of a beloved friend or family member. It's that state where all is well. No desire. No distraction. Just perfect peace with what is. A deep sense of Oneness. Aaaahhh.

I had a few glimpses into my own little personal Samadhi recently at the Millpond Music Festival in Bishop. Millpond is a great gathering of kind, conscious, peace-loving folks in a magnificent natural setting with stunning weather, great food, endless delicious music and an abundance of long, silver hair. In other words, a bunch of old hippies groovin' on life, love and music in the Sierra foothills.

However, as I contemplated the significance of my Millpond experience, I was also reminded of a bumper sticker that my dear friend has on her recumbent bike. She and her husband are cyclists. Serious cyclists. Like "riding over to the Grand Canyon and back for a week-end adventure of fun" kind of cyclists. The sticker on her bike reads, "My vacation is your worst nightmare." And so I consider the notion that although Millpond inspired my Samadhi, others might not be so agreeable. Would Liz Cheney's concept of Samadhi look like mine? Maybe not. Is Charlton Heston experiencing a blissfully endless NRA convention in his Heaven? Is my Samadhi your worst nightmare? My Heaven, your Hell? Does it really matter?

I recently read a recount from a woman who'd had a near-death experience. She had all the usual encounters: the Light, a feeling of complete peace, a sweet surrender to the Void and she even had a small conversation with what she referred to as Godhead. She asked Godhead, "What is the best religion on the planet? Which is the right religion? Christian? Catholic? Buddhist? Jewish? Hindu?" The answer she received was brilliant. Godhead replied, with the greatest love, "I don't care." Sweet.

As I reflect on my blissful glimpses at Millpond, I remind myself that Samadhi/Heaven/Nirvana is not a place, but a state of mind. Our external experience may be different, but the state of mind is the same. It's a shared consciousness. We can find perfect peace whether it's in a yoga class, NRA convention or cross-country cycling tour in the pouring rain heading uphill into a 50 mph wind. One man's ceiling is another man's floor.

The *real skill* is to have such a deep practice that you could visit all those places – folkie scene, NRA roundup, cycletopia – and still maintain that sense of perfect peace and Oneness. Like the Godhead said, "I don't care." Your Samadhi can look any way you want; it's the state of mind that counts.

Have you ever given any thought to your Samadhi? How does it feel? As you picture it, cultivate the feeling that it inspires. Develop that peace, serenity, tranquility, harmony that passes understanding. And then practice taking that feeling with you wherever you go. Hey, the longer we can carry that state of mind with us, the more pleasant Life will be, yes? And so I wonder, can I possibly retain my Millpond-inspired consciousness as I head into the DMV? A City Council meeting? Toys "R" Us?

Ah, yes. So much opportunity for practice. And Millpond only comes once a year. Drat.

ABOUT THE AUTHOR

SHANAN HARRELL, aka Yogashanan, is the Fearless Leader of the Tehachapi Yoga Tribe. She is the proud mother to Sean and Caitlin and the proud daughter of Jeri and Bob. She lives her dream life in the Tehachapi mountains of California as yoga teacher, writer and gong player (gongist?). We should all be so lucky.

Shanan Harrell
yogashanan@gmail.com
www.tehachapiyoga.com

SALT RIVER PUBLISHING

Salt River Publishing believes in encouraging artists and publishing professionals to come together and reach their empowered "Yes!"

Salt River was established with the idea of helping writers, translators, poets, graphic artists and photographers bring their work into publishable form.

We provide publishing services for anybody with a book in the making.

And we publish books that inspire and encourage, including ones that deepen the understanding of mysticism.

Do you have one?

www.SaltRiverPublishing.com

A TASTE OF SRP TITLES

The inner way

- "**A beautiful collection** of unusual stories, inspiring poetry and fresh translations of ancient texts... By turns evocative, startling, deeply moving and delightful... I open this book and so often am moved to tears: it touches that deep place of yearning within." INNER WAY, responses
- "As human beings we have a unique capacity: to expand our consciousness to its infinite potential. The mystics do not say this is easy. But they assure us it is possible..." INNER WAY, introduction
- **A taste** of selections from more than 100 mystics: **Juan de la Cruz,** "On a night of darkness, enflamed by love and yearning – O happy chance! – I slipped away undetected, my house at last grown still..." **Shiv Dayal Singh,** "What a night! What an incredible, amazing night. I'm longing to tell someone – but who will know what I'm talking about? I saw, I tasted, the Root..." **Namdev,** "When I see him, I sing – that's how this nothing of a slave became tranquil, patient: when you meet the radiance of the true master, you merge in song..." **Chuang-tse,** "The purpose of words is to convey ideas. When the ideas are grasped, the words are forgotten. Where can I find a man who has forgotten words? He is the one I would like to talk to!" INNER WAY, excerpts

Stumbling towards enlightenment

- "Shanan Harrell has stumbled onto a writing style that is at the same time quirky and profound, witty and wise, insightful and delightful... Her book is about how to be better humans in spite of our bumbling, fumbling, grumbling selves... Engaging, a giggle fest and soul-searching all at the same time." STUMBLING TOWARDS ENLIGHTENMENT, responses

- A taste: "I recently hiked the China Lake Naval Weapons Station Petroglyph Canyon. That is not a misprint."

- Taste 2: "Several years back I was invited to a very hip, über-cool party of the yoga elite in my stomping grounds of Dallas, Texas. The invitation read: *Come Celebrate Randy's Moksha!* Randy's Moksha? Is it like a Bar Mitzvah? A psychic healing? Vasectomy reversal? Should I bring a covered-dish casserole?... (I saved my Frito Pie for another party.)"

- Taste 3: "I don't remember where I first heard this particular bit of wisdom, but it's become a real favorite. I've tried to live by its high standard and I can't say I've always succeeded. I've passed it on to many and now I want to share with you this great universal precept – **Never miss a good opportunity to shut up**... So I practice the sacred art of shutting up. I remind myself to listen deeply to the other person, quiet myself, pay attention. It's a beautiful and humbling practice. And the opportunities, seriously, are endless. Now get out there and shut the hell up." STUMBLING TOWARDS ENLIGHTENMENT, excerpts

Community adventure

- "**Long Dene** was one of a small number of schools that altered the whole intellectual climate of education in England... Pioneeers like the Guinnesses changed the face of the old Victorian notion of the role of education... This book paints a lively portrait of a child's dream school, housed in a castle with a lake and endless places to explore... Amazing to think the school existed as early as 1939, with organically grown food, naturopathic healthcare, and (for the staff!) home births assisted by the community's midwife..." COMMUNITY ADVENTURE, responses

- **A taste:** One student remembers his first interview with John Guinness, founder and principal of the school: "The interview was conducted walking around the grounds in that lovely slow deliberate way he had. I felt here was a man who wouldn't panic if the whole place was on fire. He had a quiet air of confidence you could instantly respect."

- The *Denizen* 1950 issue celebrates the triumph of building **a classic open-air amphitheatre** for dance, drama, music: This was a prodigious achievement, by student volunteers, under the direction of one of the teachers. A lot of the work was done during a summer heatwave and involved getting up before 6am to put in hard labour until 7.30, when daily housework took over until breakfast... COMMUNITY ADVENTURE, excerpts

Wake up! if you can

- "The sayings of Kabir in this book give a glimpse of what it is like to go beyond all our limitations and really wake up. And the sayings also give hints on how to do it – what is required along the way... The intention of this small book of sayings is to offer – thanks to Kabir – a homeopathic dose of hope, help and humour for the way. The sayings remind us, as a contemporary mystic once said, that the path is more long than hard." WAKE UP! IF YOU CAN, introduction

- **A taste:**

> If asleep, you dream of him;
> If awake, he's in your mind:
> Eyes so immersed, Kabir,
> You're conscious only of God –
> Never separate
> Even for a moment.
>
> WAKE UP! IF YOU CAN, excerpt

Dawn has come

- "Paltu is the mystic who said about the path: 'In the game of love, whether heads or tails, it's God both ways: if I lose, I'm his – if I win, he's mine!' This saying and the songpoems of Paltu in *Dawn has come* remind us that the Naam bhakti path is a path of love – and that in love, anything is possible." DAWN HAS COME, introduction

- **A taste:**

> There's an upside-down well
> In the skies within
> Where a lamp is burning –
> A lamp is burning
> Without wick or oil...
> Dawn has come,
> A flute is playing in the skies:
> Mind – immersed, delighted...
> In the garden of Guru Gobind,
> Paltu has blossomed
> Like a flower...
>
>   DAWN HAS COME, excerpts

SALT RIVER BOOKLIST

- *The inner way: a mystic anthology of songpoems, stories, reflections* arranged with translations and notes by Anthea Guinness (SRP, 2013)
- *Stumbling towards enlightenment: a Yoga 101 collection* by Shanan Harrell (SRP, summer 2014)
- *Community adventure: the story of Long Dene School* by Sue Smithson (SRP, fall 2014)

Tuppany series
Translations of mystic writings by Anthea Guinness:
- *Wake up! if you can: sayings of Kabir* (SRP, 2014)
- *Dawn has come: songpoems of Paltu* (SRP, 2014)

www.SaltRiverPublishing.com

Published independently with Salt River assistance (editing, book design, cover design)

Books by Chloe Faith Wordsworth (Scottsdale, AZ: Resonance Publishing, 2007–2014):
- *Spiral up! 127 Energizing Options to be your best right now* (2014)
- *Quantum change made easy: breakthroughs in personal transformation, self-healing and achieving the best of who you are* (2007)
- *Empowering yourself with Resonance Repatterning,* and eleven other Resonance Repatterning practitioner books (2007–2014)

- *Dark bread and dancing: the diaries of Sue Rawson* by Rosemary Rawson (2013)

www.SaltRiverPublishing.com

COLOPHON

Typefaces: Sabon (designed by Jan Tschichold), Calli-graphic 421 (published by Bitstream), Minnie (designed by Iconian Fonts), Formal 436 (published by Bitstream)
Software: Adobe InDesign
Book Design and Composition: Carol White of **Salt River Publishing** (carol@saltriverpublishing.com)
Cover Design: Gary Mazzola (www.garymazzola.com)
Photographs: Katy Jacobson (ktzorro@sbcglobal.net)
Editing: Salt River Publishing
Printer: createspace.com
Printing method: Print-on-Demand (POD) digital printing
Paper: Library quality
Binding: Perfect binding

www.SaltRiverPublishing.com

REFLECTIONS ON READING STUMBLING TOWARDS ENLIGHTENMENT

Shanan Harrell has stumbled onto a writing style that is at the same time quirky and profound, witty and wise, insightful and delightful. *Stumbling towards Enlightenment* is a down-to-earth read about how to be better humans in spite of our bumbling, fumbling, grumbling selves. It's about reaching out, letting in and letting go in our search for our elusive, beautiful Higher Selves.

MITZI CHANDLER, author of *Gentle Reminders*

Found within these vignettes is a spiritual practice without the usual fanfare of principles and theories. Instead, they are descriptions of ordinary moments in an average day in a normal life that burst open revealing their spiritual grandeur. Shanan coaxes you to see the mystical and obscure in the ordinary. This book will change the way you perceive your neighborhood and community.

PATRICIA HUNTER, Methodist lay speaker

The combination of irreverence, wisdom, and her sharp but ever-compassionate wit make Shanan's essays engaging, a giggle fest and soul-searching all at the same time. I may not always agree with her, but she never fails to keep me stumbling right along with her.

JODI FRIEDLANDER,
co-author of *Nutrition Essentials for Everyone*

Not only is Shanan easily the best yoga teacher I have ever had, I have also never laughed harder with anyone in my life. A great thinker, great writer, great prankster!

Stumbling towards Enlightenment is a journey that chronicles the freakish path that we all take to peace.

Shanan Harrell is like the Dalai Lama, if the Dalai Lama were to live down the street from you and throw really good parties.

Yogashanan has me hooked! No... I haven't begun doing yoga poses, but I do read one chapter each morning and try to use the lesson from that chapter as I go through the day. (And I believe when I've finished the book, I will start again with the first chapter... until I get it right!) This is a funny, wise, ultimately enlightening book, which gently encourages the reader to examine his/her relationship with the world we live in. Buy it now!!!

33025728R00122

Made in the USA
Charleston, SC
02 September 2014